ACQUISITIONS

1953–62

Fully Illustrated

PUBLISHED BY ORDER OF THE TRUSTEES

Made and printed in Great Britain by
William Clowes and Sons, Limited, London and Beccles

PREFACE

THIS CATALOGUE OF ACQUISITIONS, 1953–62, includes all the pictures acquired by the National Gallery in those years. It thus forms an (overlapping) *Supplement* to the *Summary Catalogue*, which lists all the pictures in the National Gallery in July 1957. Since the first purpose is to catalogue the contents of the Exhibition of Acquisitions, 1953–62, it contains elaborate entries for the pictures included in this Exhibition, held in 1963.

THE EXHIBITION OF ACQUISITIONS, 1953–62, was able to be held without too great a disturbance of the Gallery because of the hospitality which the Tate Gallery kindly afforded to most of the British pictures normally exhibited in the great Room XVI. Even then, it seemed advisable to restrict the Exhibition to two Rooms (XVI and XVIIB). In these it was necessary to attempt a combination of a cross-section of the whole heterogeneous group of nearly 100 acquisitions with as harmonious an arrangement as possible. So it was necessary to leave in their normal places a considerable number of pictures by famous artists which should on their merits have been included in the two Exhibition Rooms. However, almost all these acquisitions are exhibited in their proper contexts in other parts of the Gallery. In the Catalogue the pictures included in the Exhibition are set in larger type, and a chronological list of the artists represented in the Exhibition will be found on page 91.

The decision to hold the Exhibition was made in March 1961, the chief purpose being to demonstrate the practical results of the attitude of recent Governments to the National Collection and gratefully to honour the enlightened persons who have been responsible for the change involved.

In the past, indeed until recently, Government policy can be described as responsible for the National Collection as a whole only to a limited extent. Two-thirds of the pictures in the National Gallery have been given or bequeathed by private persons or have been bought with money so given or bequeathed; while, if the contents of the Tate Gallery (the larger proportion gifts originating from the National Gallery and the Tate having had no purchase grant until 1946) are added, the proportion of acquisitions made from public funds is small indeed. Moreover, when in 1855 the National Gallery first received a regular Purchase Grant from the Government, this was not on a great scale in proportion to the task which had to be performed at the prices already current in those days. In most great European museums of art, the bulk of collections many times greater than that of the National Gallery was originally the property of a ruling house. In England the revolutionary Commonwealth Government dispersed almost the whole of the great collection of King Charles I. In 1824 it was after two collectors, Sir George Beaumont and the Rev. William Holwell Carr, had promised their (by such standards) little collections that the National Gallery was founded. When in 1853, after some thirty years of splendid but rather erratic acquisition by Special Grant, the purpose was formulated of making a representative collection of all the schools of painting, the new Annual Grant of £10,000 might well have seemed unrealistic. It had to be supplemented by frequent Special Grants, for of itself it would have bought very few of the pictures then in demand. For instance, in 1844 Rubens' 'Judgment of Paris' had cost £4,200, and in 1857 £12,280 had to be paid for Veronese's 'Family of Darius before Alexander'. This was considered too high a price by Parliament and the Travelling Agent was sacked; but it was to seem reasonable enough to the next generation as prices began to rise steeply in the second half of the 19th century. In 1884 the Duke of Marlborough asked £400,000 for twelve pictures, mostly by Rubens, and the National Gallery had eventually to be content with Raphael's 'Ansidei Madonna' at £70,000 and van Dyck's 'Charles I on Horseback' at £17,500. In 1890 £55,000 was the price of three portraits: Holbein's 'Ambassadors', a Moroni (No. 1316) and 'Don Adrián Pulido Pareja' (No. 1315) then believed to be by Velázquez; but Lord Rothschild, Sir Edward Guinness and Mr. Charles Cotes gave £10,000 each towards this purchase on condition that the Government would make a Special Grant of £25,000.

What has made the National Gallery unique throughout the world, however, is the collection of pictures of the Italian Gothic and Renaissance periods, which is more comprehensive than any other outside Italy; and this collection was largely made by three successive Directors with authority to spend the modest Annual Grant of £10,000. For forty years they left more fashionable pictures largely to private benefactions or to Special Grants and spent the Annual Grant boldly, often wholesale and almost exclusively, on works of this kind, which were then no more than marketable. Thus the thirty-one pictures from the Lombardi-Baldi Collection were bought by Eastlake in Florence in 1857 for £7,035. Today perhaps not one of these pictures would fail to fetch that sum, while Duccio's triptych (No. 566) and Uccello's battlepiece (No. 583) might well, each of them, fetch seven figures. Of the three pictures by Piero della Francesca in the Collection 'The Baptism' was bought by Eastlake in 1861 for £241 and the 'S. Michael' by Boxall from Eastlake's widow in 1867 for £50 (the price which Eastlake had paid for it as a private collector); Piero's 'Nativity' was acquired by Burton in 1874 among fourteen pictures bought at auction for £10,395—an average of less than £800 each. Another picture included in this purchase was Botticelli's 'Venus and Mars'. A Special Grant was necessary for it, since the

Annual Grant had been temporarily suspended in 1871. This was to recoup the Treasury for the Special Grant of £75,000 that year to buy the Peel Collection of eighty pictures. Mostly Dutch and Flemish, these pictures included Rubens' 'Chapeau de Paille' and Hobbema's 'Avenue at Middelharnis'. The bargains were not all in early Italian pictures. How much the prices of fashionable pictures had increased has already been shown. By 1894, when Burton retired, the situation was quite different with early Italian pictures also. Bode, Director since 1890 of the revitalised Berlin Museum, was in the field, the era of American private collectors was beginning and the museums of the United States had begun to amass from private benefactions their annihilating resources. Unfortunately all this coincided with Lord Rosebery's change in the administration of the Gallery. The Trustees were now given the power, and their first decision was not to take up the option offered by Lord Darnley on Titian's 'Rape of Europa', now in the Gardner Museum, Boston, perhaps the most passionate and certainly the best preserved of all Titian's late 'poesie'.

While it is the Trustees of the present day who have provided the main impetus of the revival of governmental interest in the National Collection, those of two previous generations seem to have been able to accomplish comparatively little in this respect, even under the energetic leadership of Lord Curzon, who became Chairman of a Trustees' Committee for reform in 1911. The statesman-like Curzon Report, presented unfortunately in 1914, recommended among other things an increase of the Annual Purchase Grant to £25,000. This in the light of prices then current was far too modest a claim; yet it was not until 1955–56 that the Grant was half as great. In the 20th century, though notable exceptions made possible the acquisition in 1929 of 'The Wilton Diptych' (No. 4451) and Titian's great 'Vendramin Family' (the two cost £212,000, of which the Treasury provided half), Special Grants have until recently been given at very rare intervals. The growth of the National Collection in the 20th century would have been slow and slight indeed had it not been for four great benefactors, George Salting, who in 1910 bequeathed 192 pictures of many schools, including Campin's 'Virgin with the Fire Screen', Hugh Lane, who in 1915 bequeathed the first significant French 19th-century pictures, including Renoir's 'Les Parapluies', Samuel Courtauld, who in 1923 gave a Fund of £50,000 for the purchase of French 19th-century pictures which were to include Seurat's 'Baignade', and Dr. Ludwig Mond, whose great bequest of pictures in 1924 included Raphael's early 'Crucifixion' and one of the Gallery's two small late pictures by Titian, the little 'Madonna and Child' (No. 3948). A fifth great benefactor has been the National Art-Collections Fund. Its resources are very modest in comparison with those subscribed to many individual museums in the United States; but it has played a great part in many important acquisitions, greatest of all in that of Holbein's 'Christina of Denmark', and it has given to the National Gallery 'The Rokeby Venus' by Velázquez and Leonardo's 'Virgin and Child with S. Anne and the infant S. John Baptist'.

From 1895 until 1939 what the National Gallery acquired was very little compared with what was sold abroad. It would take years to catalogue in this form the masterpieces which went from the great private collections formed here in the 18th and 19th centuries, between Titian's 'Rape of Europa' lost in 1895 and van Eyck's 'The Three Maries at the Sepulchre', now in Rotterdam, exported in 1940.

The remedial measures have come slowly and one by one. By a series of Finance Acts, dating from 1896, works of art declared to be 'of national importance' on the authority of a national museum have been exempt from estate duty as long as they remain unsold or are sold to a museum in the United Kingdom. This concession did something to delay the sale of pictures, but little to bring them to the Gallery until funds were increased and the duty represented a considerable proportion of the price. In 1939, however, it was made illegal to export works of art of more than a certain age and value without a licence from the Board of Trade, which was to seek expert advice from the Heads of National Museums; and since 1952 the Reviewing Committee on the Export of Works of Art has had the power, if an institution in the United Kingdom is willing to buy the work in question, to uphold the Board's refusal of a licence, to decide what is a fair price and to recommend the Treasury to make a grant towards the payment. Two of the acquisitions catalogued here have been made directly by means of this machinery: El Greco's 'Adoration of the Name of Jesus' and Poussin's 'Adoration of the Shepherds'. But the very existence of the machinery and the wish of the public that it should be set in motion if necessary can be seen to have played a very large part in three others: Gainsborough's 'Mr. and Mrs. Robert Andrews', Goya's 'Duke of Wellington' and Leonardo's 'Virgin and Child with S. Anne and the infant S. John Baptist'. In three of these five cases sale by auction, with the resulting publicity, preceded the acquisition and in the last the intention to sell was widely publicised. In the first case the public was taken somewhat by surprise, for it was scarcely aware of the machinery's existence, and there were complications over the price; but with each of the other four cases opinion has decidedly hardened and concern over the possibility of export has been increasingly strong.

The machinery for the control of exports is of no avail without funds; nor, when large sums have to be raised so quickly, can the public will be sufficient whether expressed through the National Art-Collections Fund or by individual benefactions. In all these cases, though in different fractions of the cost, Special Grants have been necessary from the Exchequer. The practice of Special Grants, which had been in abeyance for a generation, was revived in 1955 for the acquisition of El Greco's 'Adoration of the Name of Jesus', and another Grant was given in the following year, when the owners of 'S. John on Patmos' by Velázquez generously offered this picture to the National Gallery at a most reasonable price.

The year 1956 was of great importance to the National Collection for Section 34(1) of its Finance Act, which permitted the Inland Revenue authorities to accept chattels in lieu of payment of estate duty. The wonderful 'Pietà' by Rogier van der Weyden was the first-fruit of the Act that very year, and in the next year came the 'Donne Triptych' by Memlinc, the Gallery's one great Netherlandish triptych, and Rembrandt's 'Old Man in an Armchair'. In 1958 the double portrait by Jordaens (No. 6293) was added from the same source as the two last.

All these pictures, however, were masterpieces already well known in British collections and had been subject to the export regulations. Many pictures which the National Gallery needs must come from abroad, and this applies to French pictures of the late 19th century, which are in any case not subject to export control. The Annual Purchase Grant meanwhile had crept very slowly from £8,750 in 1953–54 (when it would still have been smaller than in the 19th century if there had been no alteration in the value of sterling and no exceptional inflation of the value of works of art) to £12,500 in 1958–59. Yet it is only when there is money in hand that bargaining can be done from strength, especially when it has to be done abroad or for pictures which are not subject to control of export. It was therefore an event of much greater importance, even than at first sight it seems, when in the financial year 1959–60 the Annual Grant was raised first to £100,000 and then to £125,000. The first rise is commemorated by Uccello's 'S. George and the Dragon', which was bought partly from a Special Grant and partly by an advance from the new Annual Grant; the second by Renoir's two famous 'Danseuses' (Nos. 6317 and 6318). These were bought largely from a Special Grant. The addition of £25,000 to the new Annual Grant of £100,000 was made retrospectively in recognition of the fact that the Trustees had arrived at an agreement with the Republic of Ireland over the Lane Bequest of 19th-century French pictures and that pictures of this school were therefore more than ever needed. In view of the prices of 19th-century French pictures in the present day, £25,000 to be spent on such pictures is a token figure; but the Chancellor promised that applications for Special Grants in this field would be given particular consideration, and the Special Grant for the two pictures by Renoir was on a handsome scale.

In the circumstances of today all the funds that have thus been made available are still less in purchasing power than the modest funds of a hundred years ago. All the Annual Grants and Special Grants made in the last ten years do not together amount to more than the funds available annually to at least one museum in the United States. An immense task lies ahead. A great many masterpieces, together worth several millions, remain in private or semi-private hands in this country which ought not to be lost from the national heritage, while in the National Gallery a great many gaps have to be filled before the Collection can be regarded as thoroughly representing at its best the history of European painting until 1900. Nevertheless, the record of these last ten years gives solid ground for hope. In terms of masterpieces, for the first time in this century far less has been lost than has been saved.

It has been saved largely by Government action. That Government has had to take a quite new degree of responsibility is not for want of public interest or of the sympathy of individuals. Of this there is ample proof in the history of the acquisition from the Royal Academy of the cartoon by Leonardo. Of the enormous sum of £800,000—the largest yet paid for any work of art—which was acquired to keep this historic masterpiece from the auction-rooms very nearly half was contributed from private sources in answer to the appeal which had to be hurriedly organised by the National Art-Collections Fund. The Pilgrim Trust out of its munificence gave £57,000, while the National Art-Collections Fund gave a similar sum. This gift, however, came from the 10,000 members of the Fund, of whom some 2,200 made special donations in addition to their normal subscriptions, and in fact, with the exception of the Pilgrim Trust's contribution, virtually the whole of this great sum was subscribed by individuals. Of these more than 24,000 are identifiable, but it is believed that almost a million persons from all over the country contributed. This is believed to be a record in the history of public subscriptions towards a single work of art. The Prime Minister's announcement of the cartoon's acquisition and of the Government's contribution of £350,000 was greeted with acclamation; and the whole episode would seem to provide good evidence of the public's interest in the two broad issues of the control of export and the continued growth of the National Collection.

Nor is the need of Special Grants on more normal occasions by any means due to lack of applications by the Gallery to potential private benefactors. But the answer to these is usually that, if so large a proportion of private wealth is taken in taxation, then either a suitable proportion of the revenue should be used in place of the private contributions which have provided the nation with most of a collection now to be valued in hundreds of millions, or some tax concessions should be granted to those who wish to carry on this great tradition.

In spite of these conditions many valuable pictures here catalogued have come to the National Gallery by gift or bequest. Goya's ill-fated 'Duke of Wellington' was largely the gift of the Wolfson Foundation, and very few of the purchases have not been assisted from funds given or bequeathed by private benefactors, by the National Art-Collections Fund, by the Pilgrim Trust or by all these generous sources together. The springs of charity are not all dry.

While the Exhibition was instituted with the purpose of honouring those who have made possible a considerable revitalisation of the National Gallery, it can achieve this result only if its contents seem a fitting return for their sympathetic effort and for the funds disbursed and expended. Before the Exhibition is examined from this angle, perhaps something may be said of the problem which today confronts any public gallery of which the terms of reference end at 1900. Even with unlimited funds it would not be possible, as it was to a certain extent a century ago, to lay down a plan of acquisition and to execute it. In the National Gallery *Report* of 1956–58 some attempt was made, in discussing the main deficiencies of the Collection, to suggest lines on which it could be made more coherent and could be further developed in accordance with the developments in art and in taste; but it was never imagined that these lines could be followed consistently or that it would not be necessary to diverge from them. It is notoriously more difficult now to find great pictures than to find money to buy them. The collectors of today must be opportunists above all. To speak of the 'art market' is to invite misunderstanding if the term seems to include pictures of great value painted before 1900. The opportunities to buy these occur at long intervals, sometimes suddenly, when there are no funds to hand, but usually after a long period of preparatory effort in various directions. To acquire some of the best pictures in the Exhibition took several years.

In the *Report* of 1956–58 it was pointed out that, Poussin and Claude apart, the French painters have been much neglected although they have provided a tradition, second only to the Italian, which must surely be represented in any comprehensive collection. In the eyes of most people today this tradition culminated in the second half of the 19th century; so that a representation of French 19th-century painting more proportionate to that of, say, the Venetian 16th century is one of the great needs of the Gallery. But where are the pictures to be bought? We were lucky indeed to intercept Cézanne's '*La Vieille au Chapelet*' between Paris and New York in 1954. The price paid was criticised immediately, but since then Government sanction to bid up to four times as much for two important pictures by Cézanne which appeared on the London market was of no avail. If those who have criticised the price of the two full-length, life-size figures by Renoir (Nos. 6317–18), for which a Special Grant of £163,500 was made in 1961, would inform us where works of this quality are to be found at lower prices, they would deserve to be placed high on the list of National Gallery benefactors. Such great pictures of this school are with very few exceptions indeed already in the museums or pledged to them.

Nevertheless a glance at the chronological list of the painters represented in the Exhibition (p. 91) will show that there have been opportunities during the last decade, and a comparison with pp. 33–44 of the 1956–58 *Report* will show that the opportunities seized have not always been out of relation with a plan to make good the deficiencies in representation. Many of the opportunities could not have been taken, some of them would not even have occurred, if the National Gallery had not received much more sympathetic treatment from the Government than it did in the earlier part of the century.

Since the Exhibition includes a great part of the Acquisitions and the exhibited pictures are catalogued in some detail, this *Catalogue of Acquisitions, 1953–62*, will be found useful as a supplement to the twelve-volume *Detailed Catalogue* and the complementary volumes of *Plates* (of the 12 volumes two remain to be published, those of the XVII century Italian and Flemish Schools, while the French School Catalogue of 1957 does not include the 19th century French pictures subsequently transferred from the Tate Gallery). The Catalogue has been compiled under my editorship by Martin Davies, Head of the Department of Early Italian and Netherlandish Painting, Cecil Gould, Head of the Department of Italian XVI century and of French XIX century Painting, Michael Levey, Head of the Department of Italian XVII and XVIII century Painting, of French Painting to 1800, of British and of German Painting, and by Gregory Martin of the Department of Flemish, Dutch and Spanish Painting. I have amplified their writings and modified them, freely in some cases, in the interests of uniformity; but the scholarship is theirs. Since acquisitions made late in 1962 are included and the Catalogue first went to press in October, there has been no great opportunity for scholarship in connection with many of the more recent; indeed the travel and research which are necessary to provide full information have varied with each entry. The compilation of the summary entries is the work of Allan Braham, Assistant Keeper II.

PHILIP HENDY
Director

ALBRECHT ALTDORFER
before 1480–1538

German School. He was probably born at Regensburg in Bavaria, where he certainly worked and where he died. He was not only a painter and etcher but an architect; indeed he was the city architect of Regensburg, where he was also a councillor. He was influenced by Dürer and by Cranach; but he is an entirely independent, even revolutionary, artist and a pioneer in pure landscape painting and in his response to natural phenomena. His earliest works date from 1507 and already the landscape interest is predominant. His drawings and etchings show, if anything, a keener response to scenery, catching the wild beauty of the landscape along the Danube, along which he travelled in 1511. He also worked as an engraver. Altdorfer is not only the leading painter of the 'Danube School' but is among the few indisputably great German painters.

6320 LANDSCAPE WITH A FOOTBRIDGE

Oil on vellum attached to wood, $16\frac{1}{2} \times 14$ ($0\cdot420 \times 0\cdot355$). Cleaned and restored on acquisition. The foliage is well preserved, but the remainder of the picture is much retouched[1].

Signed with Altdorfer's monogram extreme top right: *A A*.

There are only two surviving pure landscape paintings by Altdorfer: this and another, smaller scene in the Alte Pinakothek, Munich. His landscape interests are already apparent in his earliest works in the first decade of the 16th century, but it was probably not until later that he painted landscape by itself alone. The development is apparent first probably in water-colours of pure landscape (a fine example, dated 1522, is in the Boymans-van Beuningen Museum, Rotterdam). Our picture has been dated 1522–23 by Baldass,[2] who puts it earlier than the Munich landscape, and this order seems certain.[3] Baldass has also mentioned the present picture's analogies with Altdorfer's earlier work,[4] and it may well be that it was painted some time before 1522. Analogies with landscapes in some of the pictures executed for S. Florian (of 1518) suggest that *ca.* 1518 or even earlier may be the more likely period for its execution.

The picture was first published in 1923,[5] when it was in the possession of Messrs. Böhler, Munich, who were the owners in 1938. Later it was in the collection of Dr. Jacques Koerfer, Berne. It was bought out of the Annual Grant from Dr. Koerfer through Messrs. Nathan, Zürich, in 1961.

EXHIBITED: 1938, Munich, *Albrecht Altdorfer und sein Kreis*, No. 45.

NOTES: (1) In particular, the upper part of the building and of the sky; the upper window and the mountain are largely reconstructed. (2) L. von Baldass, *Albrecht Altdorfer*, 1941, p. 319. (3) It is also given by O. Benesch, *Der Maler Albrecht Altdorfer*, 1939, p. 26. (4) Baldass, *op. cit.*, p. 166. (5) M. Friedländer, *Albrecht Altdorfer*, 1923, p. 127.

POMPEO GIROLAMO BATONI
1708–1787

Italian School. Born at Lucca. At about the age of twenty he went to study painting in Rome, where he was to remain active until his death. In 1735 he received his first major commission, for the altar-piece of S. Gregorio Magno. From the forties onwards he was fully employed both on subject pictures and on the portraits which made him the most sought after portrait-painter in Rome. These, especially the portraits of Englishmen on the 'Grand Tour', are the best-known aspect of his art. Recent research, however, has turned to study the full range of his *œuvre* and to rediscover his important role in the development of neo-classicism, first in Rome and then in France and England. He was one of its leading exponents. The two pictures recently acquired and catalogued here represent the two chief aspects of his art. Hitherto his work was not represented in the Gallery.

6308   MR. SCOTT OF BANKSFEE

Oil on canvas, 39¾ × 29 (1·010 × 0·737). Cleaned on acquisition. In perfect condition.

Signed and dated: *P. BATONI PINXIT ROMAE/ANNO 1774.* (the *AE* in monogram).

The identity of the sitter is traditional; it is by no means certainly established.

The picture was bequeathed, in memory of her husband, by Mrs. E. M. E. Commeline, 1960.

6316   TIME DESTROYING BEAUTY

Oil on canvas, 53¼ × 38 (1·353 × 0·965). Apparently in excellent condition. Inscribed: *P.B. 1746.*

At the bidding of Time, the old woman (Jealousy?) tears at Beauty's face. For the figure of Beauty Batoni has freely transposed the marble statue of S. Susanna by François Duquesnoy in S. Maria di Loreto, Rome.[1]

This picture and a pendant, '*La Lascivia*', which is perhaps 'Beauty ravishing Wealth' in Leningrad (see below), were painted for G. B. Talenti, of Batoni's native Lucca. Correspondence between artist and patron survives, but is largely unpublished. No. 6316 is dated 1746, and the pair were completed by February 1747.

No. 6316 was in the sale of Count Koucheleff Besborodko, London, 7 July 1869 (lot 3), where it was apparently bought in.[2] Lot 2 in the same sale was a smaller 'Time revealing Truth' by Batoni. On the back of these two pictures are painted the old collection numbers *187* (No. 6316) and *188*, and these fit with the Nos. *186* and *189* on the back of two other Allegories by Batoni in the Hermitage Gallery, which are also from the Besborodko Collection. By 1959 No. 6316 was with Thomas Agnew and Son, from whom it was bought out of the Martin Colnaghi Fund in 1961.

EXHIBITED: 1960–61, Paris, Petit Palais, *La Peinture Italienne au XVIIIe Siècle*, No. 54.

NOTES: (1) A. M. Clark in the *Burlington Magazine*, 1959, p. 232 ff. He fully discusses the picture and was the first to publish it. (2) E. K. Waterhouse kindly drew attention to this provenance, hitherto unpublished.

LOUIS-EUGÈNE BOUDIN
1824–1898
French School; worked mostly in Normandy

6309, 6310 LA PLAGE À TROUVILLE

Oil on panel. No. 6309, $8\frac{1}{2} \times 18\frac{1}{8}$ (0·216 × 0·458), painted on part of a piece of carved panelling. No. 6310, $7\frac{3}{16} \times 18\frac{3}{16}$ (0·182 × 0·462). Both apparently in excellent condition.

Both signed: *E. Boudin.*

These two pictures, in addition to their intrinsic merit, have an added interest in that they once belonged to Claude Monet. Boudin was Monet's master and in a real sense the guiding spirit of his early career. He encouraged him to paint in the open air and in particular to stress the value of the first impression. As is well known, the term 'Impressionist' was first applied to the movement after the word had been used by Monet in the title of one of his pictures ('Impression, Sunrise' of 1872). The evolution of Monet from Boudin can be studied conveniently in the Gallery as there is an early work by Monet of the same subject as these two pictures—the *Plage de Trouville* (No. 3951). Monet's version, in which the figures are unusually prominent for him, shows bright sunlight and is appropriately more brilliant in handling; but few painters have equalled Boudin in reproducing the grey light of the Channel.

Nos. 6309–10 are said to have been given by Boudin to Claude Monet. They were sold by his son, Michel Monet, to a dealer, who sold them to Arthur Tooth & Sons. In 1937 they were bought from Tooth by the 1st Viscount Rothermere. Bequeathed by him in 1940 to Miss Judith E. Wilson,[1] they were bequeathed by

Miss Wilson to the Tate Gallery in 1960, and transferred together with Nos. 6311–13.

NOTE: (**1**) Information kindly supplied by Mr. Dudley Tooth.

6311 VILLAGE AU BORD D'UNE RIVIÈRE

Oil on panel, 15½ × 8 (0·394 × 0·203).
Signed: *E. Boudin*.

This and the two following pictures, 6312 and 6313, were also bequeathed in 1960 by Miss Judith E. Wilson to the Tate Gallery and transferred.

6312 LA PLAGE DE TROUVILLE

Oil on panel, 11¾ × 6 (0·298 × 0·152).
Signed: *E(?). Boudin 73*, and inscribed: *Trouville*.

6313 LAVEUSES AU BORD DE L'EAU

Oil on panel, 9 × 7 (0·229 × 0·178).
Signed: *E(?) Boudin*.

BERNARDO CAVALLINO
1616–1654/6

Neapolitan School. Born at Naples, where he studied under Andrea Vaccaro and Massimo Stanzioni. He was influenced also by Artemisia Gentileschi, who worked at Naples contemporaneously, and by Ribera. He was an admirer of the great Venetians, and Rubens was yet another influence. From all these elements Cavallino contrived to produce an elegant individual style of his own, notable for its delicate and subtle colour harmonies. For the brief period of his active life, he was the most distinguished and attractive painter in Naples. He died apparently in the outbreak of plague that also killed his master Stanzioni.

6297 THE FINDING OF MOSES

Oil on canvas, 36 × 52 (0·917 × 1·321). Cleaned on acquisition. In good condition.[1]

The subject is certainly from *Exodus*, I, vv. 1–9, even if the landscape is far from Nilotic. The predominantly rocky character of the scene separates it from two other pictures of the same subject by Cavallino.[2] The handling of the paint, moreover, seems to have divergences from that of his other paintings. In the National Gallery 'Christ driving the Money-changers from the Temple' (No. 4778) is certainly from his hand, but its present condition makes comparison unsatisfactory. Some doubt on the attribution of No. 6297 to Cavallino has been cast by at least one scholar;[3] and it is conceivable that the picture is rather by one of his

Neapolitan contemporaries. The work of the majority of these has not been exhaustively studied as yet. However, the group on the left, with Pharaoh's daughter and presumably the sister of Moses, who was bidden to find him a nurse and brought their mother, is typical of Cavallino's spare and graceful figures; moreover, the colour-scheme as a whole has his delicate and individual quality.

The picture was in an anonymous sale, London, 30 April 1958 (lot 159), as by Rosa. It was bought by Weitzner, from whom it was bought in 1959 out of Grant-in-Aid with a contribution from the Martin Colnaghi Fund.

EXHIBITED: June–August 1962, Barnard Castle, Bowes Museum, *Neapolitan and Baroque Painting*, No. 36.

NOTES: (**1**) Some retouching was necessary. In the foreground, near the foot of the kneeling maidservant in yellow, are some faint painted marks resembling the remains of a (spurious?) monogram of Salvator Rosa. (**2**) One is recorded in the Wenner Collection, Naples, the other in the Landes-museum, Brunswick. They are reproduced by A. de Rinaldis, *Bernardo Cavallino (Sei e Settecento Italiano*, 1921, No. 3), Pls. VII and XVIII. (**3**) See the comment of W. R. Juynboll in *Bulletin Museum Boymans-van Beuningen*, 1960, No. 3, p. 85.

PAUL CÉZANNE
1839–1906

French School; worked chiefly in Paris and in the country near Paris and near Aix-en-Provence.

6195 LA VIEILLE AU CHAPELET

Oil on canvas, $31\frac{3}{4} \times 25\frac{3}{4}$ (0·81 × 0·655). Apparently in excellent condition, except for the spotty discoloration of the background below the right elbow, caused by droplets from Cézanne's stove (see below).[1]

The model was formerly a servant of Jean-Marie Demolins, a notary of Aix-en-Provence.[2] The first owner of the picture, Joachim Gasquet, seems to have romanced rather freely about her when he published his book on Cézanne a generation later.[3] There, perhaps in order to represent the crotchety Cézanne as another Rembrandt in his sympathy with his models, he describes her as a demented renegade nun, whom the artist had taken into his household out of pity. The old woman must at least have spent very many hours in the studio at the Jas de Bouffan, the large house outside Aix-en-Provence where Cézanne lived and worked, for he evidently laboured again and again over the execution, piling up the thin layers of paint, one upon the other, until there is a crust which stands out obviously in places above the thinner painting of the head and hands. In an early article published in July 1896 Gasquet wrote 'the painter has just finished a canvas which is a sheer masterpiece', and went on to describe No. 6195.[4] He had sent a copy of this article to Cézanne in June,[5] and the picture must therefore have been painted before then. Presumably it was in fact finished some months before, for in his book of 1921 Gasquet described how he came into possession of the canvas:

'For eighteen months at the Jas de Bouffan he worked furiously at the ' *Vieille au Chapelet*'. When the canvas was finished he chucked it into a corner. It got covered with dust, rolled on the floor, despised, heedlessly trodden on. One day I found it. I came upon it under the coalscuttle by the stove, with the zinc pipe gently steaming and dripping on to it at five-minute intervals. What miracle had preserved it intact I don't know. I cleaned it, and the poor old girl appeared before me. . . .'[6]

The present appearance of the picture fully bears out this account, for the condition in the bottom left corner was attributed to the action of steam by the Chief Restorer before he was aware of Gasquet's description. Similarly, the thick and wrinkled paint supports his account of the long gestation. Gasquet's early article, together with a letter to him from Cézanne, substantiates his later statement that the picture was painted at the Jas de Bouffan, that is before 1899, when the estate was sold; this has been doubted recently by most art-historians.[7] No. 6195 is indeed far from being one of his last works.

Gasquet was thus not altogether a romancer, and in view of the extreme rarity of an account by any great artist of the gestation of one of his pictures, he must be quoted on this subject at least in a footnote, while we remember the poetic licence that he probably exercised in describing the sitter.[8]

Later, the picture is said to have been owned by Henri Bernstein, the playwright. By February 1910 it was with the Galerie E. Druet, Paris, who still owned it in 1912. By October 1917 it belonged to Jacques Doucet, founder of the Bibliothèque d'Art et d'Archéologie in Paris which is known by his name. From Doucet's heirs it was bought in 1953 through César de Hauke out of the Grant-in-Aid and Florence, Temple-West, Clarke, Hornby Lewis and Champney Funds.

EXHIBITED: 1907, Paris, Salon d'Automne, *Exposition Cézanne*, p. 250, No. 47; 1910–11, London, Grafton Galleries, 'Manet and the Post-Impressionists', No. 13; 1912, Frankfort, *Die Klassische Malerei Frankreichs im 19. Jahrhundert*, No. 5; 1912, Paris, Salon d'Automne, *Exposition de Portraits du XIXe Siècle*, p. 225, No. 49; 1917, Zürich, *Französische Kunst*, No. 21; 1920, Paris, Bernheim-Jeune, *Cézanne*, No. 1; 1926, Amsterdam, *Art Français*, No. 3; 1935, Brussels, Palais des Beaux-Arts, *L'Impressionisme*, No. 6; 1936, Paris, Orangerie, *Cézanne*, No. 105; 1939, New York, Museum of Modern Art, *Art in our Time*, No. 63; 1947, Cincinnati, *Cézanne*, No. 11; 1953, Aix-en-Provence and Nice, *Cézanne*, No. 23; 1954, Edinburgh Festival and Tate Gallery, Arts Council, *Cézanne*, No. 57.

NOTES: (1) Cleaned probably in 1953, before acquisition or before the exhibition of that year. (2) In a letter to Gasquet, the then owner, dated Aix, 12 May 1902, Cézanne asked him to lend to an exhibition organised by the Société des Amis des Arts of Aix ' *la tête de vieille, ex-bonne de Marie Demolins*'. The letter is published in full by John Rewald, *Cézanne, Geffroy et Gasquet*, etc., 1959, p. 43. (3) Joachim Gasquet, *Cézanne*, 1921, pp. 66–67 and 82. (4) Demolins was associated with Gasquet in a literary review dedicated to Provence and called *Les mois dorés*. The article appeared in the second monthly number. The relevant parts are reprinted by Rewald, *op. cit.*, pp. 28–30. (5) Rewald, *op. cit.*, p. 27. (6) Gasquet, *loc. cit.*, freely translated by P. H. (7) Ambroise Vollard, *Paul Cézanne*, 1914, Pl. 42, dates it 1896; J. Meier-Graefe, *Cézanne und sein Kreis*, 4th ed., 1920, p. 201, also 1896; Georges Rivière, *Le Maître Paul Cézanne*, 1923, p. 221, also 1896; L. Venturi, *Cézanne*, 1936, Vol. I, No. 702, p. 216, dates it 1900–04; Bernard Dorival, *Cézanne*, 1948, p. 173, No. 161, dates it 1900–06; Douglas Cooper in *The Burlington Magazine*, Vol. XCVI, 1954, p. 380, dates it 1898–1900; Martin Davies, National Gallery Catalogues, *French School*, 2nd ed., 1957: 'very near in style to the portrait of Vollard (1899) now in the Petit Palais, Paris'. (8) Gasquet, *loc. cit.*: 'You know', Gasquet tells us that Cézanne said to him, 'that when Flaubert was writing

Salammbo he said he saw purple. Well! When I was painting my *Vieille au Chapelet* I saw a Flaubert tone, an atmosphere, something indefinable, a colour bluish and reddish which comes out of *Madame Bovary*, I think. I tried reading Apuleius to chase away this obsession, which at one moment seemed dangerous, too literary. It was no good. This great blue red was too much for me. It sang in my soul. I was completely bathed in it.' Gasquet asked if this colour came between Cézanne and reality, between his eyes and the model. 'Not a bit. It floated, as anywhere else. I scrutinised all the details of the costume, the cap, the folds of the apron; I deciphered the sly face. It was definitely afterwards that I remembered the description of the old servant at the agricultural meeting. What I am trying to explain to you is something more mysterious, entangled in the very roots of one's being, at the impalpable source of one's senses' (again, very freely translated by P. H.). The old woman in *Madame Bovary* 'had huge wooden clogs on her feet and a great blue apron across her hips. Her thin face, surrounded by a hemless hood, had more creases and wrinkles than a shrivelled rennet apple, and the sleeves of her red blouse came down over two long hands'.

Philippe de CHAMPAIGNE
1602–1674

French School. Born in Brussels; went in 1621 to Paris, where he settled. He became a founder member of the Académie Royale in 1648.

6276 THE VISION OF S. JOSEPH

Oil on canvas, $82\frac{1}{4} \times 61\frac{1}{4}$ ($2 \cdot 085 \times 1 \cdot 555$). There are additions on canvas inserted later at the top corners to make the picture rectangular; but the painting appears otherwise to be in excellent condition.

The subject is from *Matthew*, I, v. 18 *et seq*. The Angel of the Lord appears to the sleeping Joseph and reveals to him the mystery of the Incarnation.

The style of the picture blends such Flemish or Caravaggesque elements as the emphasis on S. Joseph's carpentry tools and the dramatic Angel with a more classical manner, represented by the figure of the Virgin. In Champaigne's later work the classical manner becomes more pronounced. This suggests a date from about 1635, or a little later. By that time Champaigne had attracted the patronage of King Louis XIII and of Cardinal Richelieu. In the Gallery are two portraits of Richelieu by Champaigne;[1] but this is the first subject picture by him—and indeed the first full-scale altarpiece of the French 17th century School—to enter the Collection.

Champaigne painted at least three pictures of this subject.[2] It is probable that this is the altarpiece painted for the church of the Minims,[3] now demolished but then newly built near what is now the Place des Vosges, Paris; an altarpiece there of the subject by Champaigne is mentioned in early guide-books. That picture was removed at the time of the Revolution[4] and was sold by auction in 1797–98 (*4 Vendémaire, An VI*). In 1841 No. 6276 was almost certainly one of eleven pictures by Champaigne in the vast collection of Napoleon's uncle, Cardinal Fesch (No. 416), and on 28 March 1845 it was in his sale in Rome (lot 38), bought by Warneck. In this catalogue it was described as brought from France and (almost certainly in error) as from the church of the Oratoire. Later it was in the Furtado de Heine Collection. In 1913, December 22–23, No. 6276 was in the sale of Princess Ney de la Moscowa, Paris (lot 79); and in 1919, May 22, it was in an anonymous sale there.

It was bought from Jacques Seligman and Co. in 1957 out of the Temple-West, Florence, Hornby-Lewis, Clarke and Champney Funds.

EXHIBITED: 1951, Pittsburgh, Carnegie Institute, *French Painting 1100–1900*, No. 65, lent by Seligman; 1952, Paris, Orangerie, *Philippe de Champaigne*, No. 16; 1953, New York, Seligman, *XVII Century French Paintings*, No. 3.

ENGRAVING: P. Lombart (*ca.* 1613–82) in reverse.

VERSION: Lot 39 in the sale of Cardinal Fesch, Rome, 28 March 1845, was a small sketch by Champaigne.

NOTES: (**1**) No. 798, triple portrait head and shoulders only; No. 1449, full-length. (**2**) Another, commissioned for the Carmel, Faubourg Saint Jacques, Paris, is now at Bordeaux; a third was painted for the church of the Oratoire. The Oratoire picture was almost certainly smaller than No. 6276. For fuller discussion see Dorival in the Catalogue of the 1952 Exhibition (above, under EXHIBITED), p. 48. (**3**) Recorded in the church of the Minims in the inventory of 20 December 1790; see *Nouvelles Archives de l'Art Français*, 3rd series, Vol. VI, 1890, p. 96. (**4**) Dépôt des Monuments Français, No. 130; see *Revue Universelle des Arts*, 1865, Vol. 21, p. 81.

PIETER CLAESZ.
1596/7–1661

Dutch School; worked at Haarlem.

Ascribed to PIETER CLAESZ.

6336 STILL LIFE

Oil on canvas, 33¾ × 39¾ (0·858 × 1·010).
Bequeathed by Claude Dickason Rotch, 1962.

GONZALES COQUES
1614–1684

Flemish School; worked in Antwerp.

Ascribed to GONZALES COQUES

6160 PORTRAIT OF A YOUNG LADY IN BLACK

Oil on oak, 7⅞ × 6⁹⁄₁₆ (0·202 × 0·107).
Mrs. Charles Carstairs Bequest, 1952; entered the Collection in 1953.

JEAN-BAPTISTE-CAMILLE COROT
1796–1875

French School; worked in the Fontainebleau region and elsewhere in France and Italy.

6339 DARDAGNY—UN CHEMIN DANS LA CAMPAGNE, LE MATIN

Oil on canvas, 10¼ × 18½ (0·260 × 0·470).
Presented by William Edward Brandt, Henry Augustus Brandt, Walter Augustus Brandt and Alice Marie Bleecker in memory of Rudolph Ernst Brandt, 1962.

6340 LA CHARRETTE, SOUVENIR DE SAINTRY

Oil on canvas, 18½ × 22⅜ (0·470 × 0·569).
Signed and dated: *COROT 1874*.
Presented by William Edward Brandt, Henry Augustus Brandt, Walter Augustus Brandt and Alice Marie Bleecker in memory of Rudolph Ernst Brandt, 1962.

Charles-François DAUBIGNY
1817–1878

French School; worked at Auvers, near Pontoise, and elsewhere in France.

6323 VIEW ON THE OISE WITH BOAT AND LAUNDRESS

Oil on canvas, 15¼ × 26 (0·388 × 0·661).
Signed and dated: *Daubigny 1873*.
Bequeathed in 1928 by Pandeli Ralli, with a life interest to his niece, Viscountess Byng of Vimy; entered the Collection in 1961.

6324 LANDSCAPE WITH CATTLE BY A STREAM

Oil on canvas, 14 × 26 (0·356 × 0·661).
Signed and dated: *Daubigny 1872*.
Bequeathed by Pandeli Ralli, 1928 (cf. No. 6323 above).

Hilaire-Germain-Edgar DEGAS
1834–1917

French School. He was in Rome 1856–57, and thereafter worked in Paris.

6295 APRÈS LE BAIN, FEMME S'ESSUYANT

Pastel on paper, 40½ × 39 (1·028 × 0·991). Apparently in excellent condition.
Stamped: *Degas*.
One of a considerable number of similar studies by Degas, though most were on a smaller scale. The models are variously shown combing, spongeing or drying themselves, nearly always from the back or from another angle which does not reveal the features. Very few of these pastels are dated; but most of them were produced in the ten or fifteen years from about the mid-1880's. Degas' eyesight

was then beginning to be seriously affected and he was turning more and more to pastels. These studies in general, and the present one in particular, show his art in an unusually monumental vein. Sir Kenneth Clark has traced the origin of this pose to that of a soldier fastening his armour in Michelangelo's lost cartoon of the 'Battle of Cascina'.[1]

The pastel is No. 955 in P. A. Lemoisne's *Degas et son Œuvre* (1946). It was lot 115 in the Degas sale, Paris, 11–13 December 1918; lot 74 in the Georges Viau sale, Paris, 11 December 1942 (reproduced). It was bought about 1950 from the Lefevre Gallery, London, by Harry Walston, from whom it was purchased through the Lefevre Gallery in 1959.

EXHIBITED: May–June 1950, London, Lefevre Gallery, No. 9 (reproduced); 1951–52 and 1958, Tate Gallery, lent by Mrs. Walston.
NOTE: (1) Sir Kenneth Clark, *The Nude*, 1956, p. 211.

FERDINAND-VICTOR-EUGÈNE DELACROIX
1798–1863

French School. The leading 'Romantic'. Worked mostly in Paris.

6262   OVID AMONG THE SCYTHIANS

Oil on canvas, 34½ × 54¼ (0·88 × 1·30). Apparently in excellent condition.[1]
Signed and dated: *Eug.Delacroix./1859.*
Ovid is resting on the ground towards the left. The Latin poet was banished to Tomis or Tomi, the modern Constantza, near the mouth of the Danube, in A.D. 8; he is thought to have died there about A.D. 17/18. Some description of his dreary life at Tomis is included in the *Tristia* and *Epistulae ex Ponto* which he sent to Rome; but Delacroix seems to have paid little or no attention to the details thus available. The milking of the mare in the foreground is derived rather from classical statements that the Scythians fed on mare's milk.[2] As Baudelaire pointed out, Delacroix's feelings on this subject would seem to be paralleled by passages of Châteaubriand's *Les Martyrs*.[3]

The subject of Ovid in exile had been in Delacroix's mind at intervals for some twenty years. He had used it for one of the pendentives in the Library of the Chambre des Députés in Paris, dating from 1838 onwards.[4] The composition there is different; but there are at least two drawings of pendentive shape related to No. 6262, to show that he had considered using a similar composition for the Library.[5] He must have worked on the present composition again about 1855, for in a letter of 11 March 1856 he writes of a sketch carried out about a year before.[6] In 1856 it was agreed that No. 6262 should be painted when Benoît Fould expressed a wish for a picture from his hand; and he had made some progress with it by 26 May 1856.[7] Yet it was still not finished in late January 1859.[8]

However, it was exhibited in 1859 at the Salon. With the rest of Delacroix's pictures there, No. 6262 had a poor reception from the regular critics. Baudelaire came to his support with extra vehemence. Of this picture, to which he devoted an unusual amount of space, he wrote among other things: 'It can be said of "Ovid among the Scythians" that it is one of those wonderful works such as Delacroix alone can conceive and paint. The artist who has painted this can count himself a happy man, and he who is able to feast his eyes upon it every day may also call himself happy. The mind sinks into it with a slow and appreciative rapture, as it would sink into the heavens, or into the sea's horizon—into eyes brimming with thought, or a rich and fertile drift of reverie. I am convinced that this picture has a charm all its own for subtle spirits; I would be almost prepared to swear that, more than others perhaps, it must have pleased highly-strung and poetic temperaments' (trans. Jonathan Mayne in *The Mirror of Art*, Phaidon, 1955).

Benoît Fould, elder brother of Achille Fould, the prominent financier and politician who had considerable influence on Delacroix's career, had died in July 1858; but it appears that his widow had confirmed the commission.[9] The picture passed from her to a niece, Mme. de Sourdeval.[10] Her daughter married Charles Demachy, who was certainly the owner of the picture;[11] and his daughter Germaine married Baronne Ernest Seillière.[12] From the heirs of Baronne Ernest Seillière it was bought by César de Hauke. From de Hauke it was purchased out of the Colnaghi Fund in 1956.

EXHIBITED: 1859, Paris, Salon, No. 822; 1892, Paris, *Cent Chefs-d'Œuvre*, No. 63 (Memorial Volume): 1930, Paris, *Delacroix*, No. 183.

VERSIONS AND DRAWINGS: For two drawings of pendentive shape but related to No. 6262 see above and Note 5, below. For a sketch made about 1855 recorded by Delacroix, see above and Note 6. For another possible sketch and a number of drawings, see Davies, *loc. cit.* A smaller painted version of No. 6262, signed and dated 1862, was No. 375 in the Delacroix Exhibition at Zürich, 1939.[13]

NOTES: (1) The canvas has not been lined. The picture was evidently cleaned shortly before it was acquired. After acquisition the new varnish was slightly thinned. (2) For full annotation of this entry see Martin Davies, National Gallery Catalogues, *The French School*, 2nd. ed., 1957, pp. 77–79, from which the entry is adapted. (3) Charles Baudelaire, *Œuvres*, ed. J. Crépet, Vol. II, 1923, pp. 295–96. See also some remarks by Delacroix himself in his *Journal*, ed. A. Joubin, 1932, Vol. III, pp. 382–83. (4) For reproductions, etc., see Davies, *loc cit.* The subject was not in Delacroix's first plan for the decoration. Several drawings and a sketch connected with the Chambre des Députés design are known to exist. (5) For reproductions, etc., see Davies, *loc. cit.* (6) See Delacroix, *Correspondance Générale*, ed. Joubin, Vol. III, 1937, pp. 320–21. The subject had evidently been exercising his mind earlier, see his *Journal*, 10 April 1849 (Joubin, 1932, Vol. I, p. 285) and 9 December 1853. (7) *Correspondance*, ed. Joubin, III, 1937, pp. 320–21 and 322–23; *Journal*, 6 and 27 March, 14 April 1856 and (ed. Joubin, 1932, Vol. II, p. 449) 26 May 1856. (8) Delacroix's letter of 27 January 1859 in *Correspondance*, Vol. IV, p. 75. (9) This is implied in the letter of 27 January 1859 (see previous note). (10) It was Mme. de Sourdeval who lent the picture to the 1892 Exhibition (see above, under EXHIBITED). (11) Demachy ownership is recorded several times in A. Joubin's editions of the *Journal* and *Correspondance*. (12) See Davies, *loc. cit.* (13) Catalogue, Pl. XXIII; A. Robaut (and E. Chesneau), *L'Œuvre Complet de Eugène Delacroix*, 1885, No. 1439, reproduced, and p. 538. No. 6262 is Robaut, No. 1376.

JEAN-FRANÇOIS DE TROY
1679–1752

French School; worked in Paris and Rome.

6330 JASON SWEARING ETERNAL AFFECTION TO MEDEA

Canvas, $22\frac{1}{4} \times 20\frac{1}{2}$ (0·565 × 0·52). Apparently in good condition.

Jason was sent by his uncle, Pelias, to steal the golden fleece from Colchis. He succeeded in doing this through the help of the sorceress Medea, daughter of the King of Colchis, whom he later married. At the right a statue of Hecate, goddess associated with sorcery.

The subject is the first in the series of seven from the story of Jason which were used by De Troy for tapestry designs commissioned of him by the French Crown during his directorship of the French Academy in Rome;[1] they followed on his 'Esther' series. The story is taken from Ovid's *Metamorphoses*, Book VII. De Troy had proposed the history either of Solomon or of Jason as offering opportunities for 'nobility and magnificence'. Believing that the latter story would be chosen, as it was, he had by December 1742 executed the sketch of 'Jason taming the Bulls' (now in the Barber Institute, Birmingham).[2] By 11 January 1743 three of the *modelli* or sketches were completed, but the subjects are not specified. By 15 February of the same year De Troy could report all seven *modelli* finished, but he had not sent them to Paris as the bad weather was preventing them drying. He had then already prepared the canvas for the largest of the paintings to be executed from the sketches.

On reaching Paris, the sketches were considerably criticised, but the letter addressed to De Troy on this subject is unfortunately lost. On 28 June 1743 he was seeking permission to execute the large-scale pictures, modifying his designs in the light of the objections raised. He received permission in a letter of 15 July the same year. He had begun painting the largest of the pictures by August, and it was finished in January 1744. On 15 April 1744 he was working on the large picture of the present subject which was about ten feet square; it was dated 1744. It was in the museum at Brest until it was destroyed during the 1939–45 war.

The large-scale pictures reached Paris eventually in September 1748, and the Salon was extended for eight days longer than usual so that De Troy's pictures could be exhibited. Of the tapestries woven from the designs at the Gobelins twelve sets appear to have existed. One set is at Windsor Castle, another in the Victoria and Albert Museum. A set was used in 1770 to decorate the reception pavilion of Marie Antoinette at Strasbourg, when she was on her way to Paris to marry the Dauphin (later Louis XVI). The young Goethe saw them there and remarked on the ill-omened choice of subject for a marriage (Jason's vow of eternal affection not having proved sufficient in the face of Medea's wiles).[3] Of the seven sketches, six, including the present one, were in the De Troy sale, Paris, 9 April 1764. No. 6330 is not recorded again until 1930, when it was with the heirs of Jacques Seligmann.[4] It belonged to André Seligmann in 1937. By 1954 it belonged to Francis Falconer Madan, who bequeathed it, with other pictures, in 1962.

EXHIBITED: 1937, Paris, *Chefs d'œuvre de l'Art Français*, No. 151; 1954–55, London, R.A., *European Masters of the 18th Century*, No. 466; 1957, Manchester, *Art Treasures Centenary* Exhibition, No. 185; 1959, Rome, *Mostra del Settecento a Roma*, No. 632; 1962, London, Colnaghi's, *Francis Falconer Madan Memorial*, No. 10.

NOTES: (1) The fullest account of the genesis of the Jason series is to be found in the correspondence exchanged between De Troy in Rome and the Ministers in Paris: cf. *Correspondance des Directeurs de l'Académie de France à Rome*, Vol. X, 1900, *passim*. The details quoted in the text here derive from that source. (2) Reproduced in the exhibition catalogue of *Seventeenth and Eighteenth Century Oil Sketches*, Hazlitt Gallery, May 1961 (23); the same exhibition (22) also contained the sketch for the 'Capturing of the Golden Fleece'. (3) Cf. G. H. Lewes, *The Life of Goethe*, n.d., p. 67: Goethe did not name the designer of the tapestries but there can be no doubt that De Troy's series is meant. (4) Recorded by G. Brière in *Les Peintres Français du XVIIIe Siècle*, ed. L. Dimier, Vol. II, 1930, p. 37, No. 52.

DOMENICHINO
1581–1641

Domenico Zampieri called '*Il Domenichino*'. Bolognese School. Born at Bologna 21 or 28 October 1581. After an early apprenticeship with Calvaert he became a pupil of Ludovico Carracci, the master also of Albani and Guido Reni. His first works were painted at Bologna, under Ludovico's guidance; but early in the 17th century, perhaps in 1602, he arrived in Rome, where Albani and Reni had preceded him. Here he worked in collaboration with Annibale Carracci, Ludovico's cousin and the leader of the family. He was taken under the protection of Monsignor Agucchi and through him must have received his first major commission, for the frescoes at Villa Aldobrandini at Frascati (*e.g.* the pictures catalogued below), since the villa belonged to Agucchi's *padrone*, Cardinal Pietro Aldobrandini. In these is already revealed his pioneering interest in landscape painting.

His next major work was the fresco series at Grottaferrata, but it was with the 'Last Communion of S. Jerome' (Vatican Gallery) of 1614 and with the 'Hunt of Diana' (Borghese Gallery) that he became famous. In 1624 he began the important fresco series in S. Andrea della Valle at Rome, and in 1631 he left Rome for Naples to work on frescoes in the cathedral there. He was driven away by the jealousy of the Neapolitan artists and the unfavourable reception of his work; but he returned to Naples later and died there 6 April 1641. Domenichino's pioneer work in landscape painting influenced Claude, and his landscapes were praised by Constable. His particular brand of classicism, deeply indebted to the example of Raphael, had its effect notably on the young Poussin.

6284　APOLLO SLAYING THE NYMPH CORONIS

Fresco, $78\frac{1}{2} \times 35\frac{1}{4}$ ($1 \cdot 994 \times 0 \cdot 895$). Transferred from a canvas support to hardboard and cleaned 1958–62. In good condition. Nos. 6285–91 were treated in the same way.[1]

Coronis of Larissa in Thessaly was loved by Apollo, whose child she was to bear; but she was detected in infidelity by Apollo's raven, and the god, who eventually cursed the raven black, shot her with his bow and arrow. He regretted it too late.

This and the seven following pictures, Nos. 6285–91, are all from the same series representing episodes from the legend of Apollo, mostly as they are told by the Roman poet Ovid in his *Metamorphoses*. For their history and provenance see under No. 6290.

There are three drawings for this fresco in the Royal Collection at Windsor Castle.

No. 6284 (only) was exhibited in 1962 at Bologna, *L'Ideale Classico del Seicento in Italia e la Pittura di Paesaggio*, No. 15.

6285　THE PUNISHMENT OF MIDAS

Fresco, $105\frac{1}{4} \times 80\frac{3}{4}$ ($2 \cdot 670 \times 2 \cdot 240$). In fair state, though retouching was necessary in parts of the landscape. See note 1.

Midas of Phrygia (the legendary king with the touch of gold) had to judge in a musical contest between Apollo and the silenus Marsyas (see No. 6288). Because he alone voted against Apollo, the god made him grow donkey's ears.

There are seven sheets of studies for this fresco at Windsor. The composition is based on a drawing by Annibale Carracci in the Ellesmere collection.

6286　THE TRANSFORMATION OF CYPARISSUS

Fresco, $47\frac{1}{4} \times 34\frac{3}{4}$ ($1 \cdot 200 \times 0 \cdot 883$). The upper half of this fresco remains *in situ*. No. 6286 is otherwise in good condition. See note 1.

Cyparissus (*i.e.*, Cypress), 'handsomest of the Cean boys', was so distraught at having shot a sacred stag which he adored that he begged to be allowed to mourn for ever. Apollo turned him into a tree.

A study for the figure of Apollo in the upper part of the fresco (still at Frascati) is at Windsor.

6287　APOLLO AND DAPHNE

Fresco, $123\frac{3}{4} \times 74\frac{1}{2}$ ($3 \cdot 118 \times 1 \cdot 892$). In fair condition, though retouching was necessary in parts of the landscape. See note 1.

This is the story of another tree (daphne = bay) which we owe to Apollo. He had offended Cupid, who from Mount Parnassus shot two arrows of different kinds, one into the god, who became ardent with love, the other into mortal Daphne, with the opposite effect. When they met, she fled and, when Apollo came up with her, she only prayed for transformation. He loved her even as a tree.

A closely related drawing for the whole composition is at Windsor. It is reproduced by Pope-Hennessy (see DRAWINGS below)

6288   THE FLAYING OF MARSYAS

Fresco, $81\frac{5}{8} \times 130\frac{1}{2}$ (2·102 × 3·314). In fair condition, though many minor retouchings were necessary. See note 1.

Athena invented the oboe, but threw it away because playing it distorted her face. Marsyas the silenus picked it up and in time became so proud of his playing that he challenged Apollo's lyre. The winner could do as he liked with the loser, and Apollo, who won divinely, had Marsyas flayed alive.

There are six sheets of studies for this fresco at Windsor.

6289   NEPTUNE AND APOLLO ADVISING LAOMEDON ON THE BUILDING OF TROY

Fresco, $120\frac{1}{4} \times 72\frac{1}{4}$ (3·058 × 1·834). In fair condition, though painted in an inferior manner. See note 1.

Apollo and Neptune found that Laomedon had too great a task building Troy. Disguising themselves as mortals and receiving a promise of gold for their services, they soon had the walls built. When Laomedon welched, Poseidon as quickly had the walls down again, flooding the country.

The painting here, both of the figures and of the landscape, suggests another and inferior hand, although no less than four drawings for the figures by Domenichino are at Windsor.

6290   APOLLO KILLING THE CYCLOPS

Fresco, $124\frac{1}{2} \times 75$ (3·163 × 1·904). A good deal of retouching has been necessary to the dwarf's face and over sizeable damages in the landscape. See note 1.

The frescoes were all painted to look like painted or woven hangings with gold-embroidered borders and heavy gold fringes, much as a more famous series had been nearly a century before in the 'Hall of Constantine' in the Vatican, partly designed by Raphael and painted by his followers. In this picture and in two others (Nos. 6287 and 6289) the borders have survived. In this one Domenichino has emphasised the effect of *trompe l'œil* by representing the hanging as caught against an unfortunate dwarf in chains. According to Passeri the dwarf belonged to the Aldobrandini family, and was thus portrayed as a punishment at the orders of the Cardinal.[2] A dwarf appears in the 'Hall of Constantine', but in the painted hanging not outside it.

A study for the dwarf's head is at Windsor.

These seven scenes, Nos. 6284–90, and another, No. 6291 (below), are from a series of ten, all dealing with events from the Legend of Apollo, which formed the major part of a scheme of decoration in a garden pavilion of the Villa Belvedere at Frascati, near Rome.[3] The room was dedicated to the god and at one end was a sculptured group and a fountain representing Apollo and the Muses with Pegasus on Mount Parnassus; under this was an organ. The villa was then newly built to the designs of Giacomo della Porta for Cardinal Pietro Aldobrandini, the nephew of Pope Clement VIII.

The frescoes were commissioned by the Cardinal through the good offices of Monsignor G. B. Agucchi, Domenichino's friend and the Cardinal's secretary, of whom there is a portrait by Domenichino in York. The result has been called 'Domenichino's first indubitable masterpiece'.[4] It is recorded that he was assisted by another landscape-painter, G. B. Viola (1576–1622), and by the quite obscure Alessandro Fortuna.[5] Almost certainly the execution of No. 6289 is by another artist, and there are suggestions of a feebler hand in other scenes here and there. In what is plainly by Domenichino himself there are passages showing a youthful timidity, and the style in general suggests a moment near the beginning of his career. Moreover, the artist began the great series of frescoes at Grottaferrata in 1608. Those seem more mature, and documentary sources imply that they were subsequent to the Apollo series. Pope-Hennessy[6] and Mahon[7] have both therefore proposed for the Apollo frescoes a date before 1608, and about 1605–6 is probable. This view is endorsed by Cavalli in the Catalogue of the 1962 Exhibition at Bologna, cited below. An objection to such a date has been raised recently and the execution placed no earlier than 1611. For this the grounds are that in a letter, undated but datable about then, from Cardinal Aldobrandini to his friend Duke Charles of Savoy the decorations of the villa are mentioned in some detail, but not the Apollo frescoes.[8] Evidence drawn from a *lacuna* of this nature has often proved dangerous; and the facts that Domenichino was only a very young man and became famous only with his 'Last Communion of S. Jerome', now in the Vatican Gallery, of 1614 have been given as a sufficient reason for the Cardinal's silence in respect of him.

In spite of the tentative and youthful quality of many of these compositions and of the subsequent ravages of time, Domenichino is revealed here as a landscape-painter of originality and of considerable importance in the School of Rome.

In the early 19th century (probably until about 1840) the frescoes remained in the Villa Aldobrandini and visitors were permitted to dine in the pavilion. By 1847 they were no longer to be seen there.[9] They had been detached and moved probably to the Palazzo Borghese in Rome, where they are mentioned by Burckhardt in 1855.[10] The somewhat ambiguous wording of his text is clarified by a guide-book of 1857, where they are simply said to have been transferred to Rome.[11] In 1892 they were sold in Rome and acquired by the late Count Karl Lanckoronski.[12] They decorated the walls of a large room filled with antique sculpture in the Lanckoronski Palace in Vienna until 1945, when the palace was burnt. They were removed in time and eventually stored at Schloss Hohenems in Switzerland. There they were bought in 1958 from Count Antoine Lanckoronski (see also under No. 6294, Uccello) out of the Annual Grant-in-Aid with a contribution from the Colnaghi Fund.

ENGRAVINGS: The frescoes were all engraved by D. Barrière for *Villa Aldobrandina Tusculana*, 1647.

DRAWINGS: In the Royal Collection at Windsor Castle there are twenty-eight sheets of drawings by Domenichino for this series of frescoes, including the two scenes remaining *in situ*. They share the youthful and tentative nature of the frescoes, with which they are homogeneous in style. See John Pope-Hennessy, *Domenichino Drawings at Windsor Castle*, 1948, Nos. 1097–1124.

NOTES: (**1**) A modicum of plaster, about $\frac{1}{16}$ in. thick, has survived. This was attached when the frescoes were taken from the walls—or at least long before the pictures were acquired—to canvas fixed upon inadequate wooden stretchers. The stretchers and canvas have now been removed and the plaster film affixed to two layers of synthetic board, with expanded paper between. All the frescoes were very dirty and all have been cleaned, except No. 6291 (see below), which has been cleaned only superficially. A good deal of discoloured retouching of various periods has been removed, and a considerable amount of new retouching has been necessary. On the whole, however, with the exception of No. 6291, the pictures are in fair condition. (**2**) J. Hess, *Die Kunstlerbiographien von G. B. Passeri*, 1934, p. 26. (**3**) See the very full discussion by Cavalli in the Catalogue of the Exhibition, *L'Ideale Classico del Seicento in Italia e la Pittura di Paesaggio*, under No. 15 (No. 6284, see above) and pp. 75–76. (**4**) Pope-Hennessy, *op cit.*, p. 14. (**5**) J. Hess, *loc. cit.* (**6**) Pope-Hennessy, *op. cit.*, p. 95. (**7**) Mahon in the Catalogue of the *Mostra dei Carracci: Disegni*, Bologna, 1956, No. 127. See also his discussion in the Catalogue of the Exhibition *Dessins des Carrache*, Paris, 1961, p. 57 *et seq.* (**8**) See note 2. (**9**) Cf. Nibby-Vasi, *Itinerario di Roma* (ed. Valenti), 1847, II, p. 738. Attention to this and to the facts following above was drawn by D. Mahon while this catalogue was in proof. (**10**) See J. Burckhardt, *Der Cicerone*, 1855, p. 1045. (**11**) Nibby-Vasi, French edition, 1857, p. 641. (**12**) They were published by H. Tietze in *Ausgewählte Kunstwerke der Sammlung Lanckoronski*, 1918, p. 71, *et seq.*

6291 MERCURY STEALING THE HERDS OF ADMETUS GUARDED BY APOLLO

Fresco transferred from canvas to hardboard, 103 × 79½ (2·616 × 2·019). This picture has been only superficially cleaned since it was acquired, being extensively damaged and repainted. Not enough of the original survives to justify in present circumstances the long operation of thorough cleaning and restoration. Little can be said about the execution in its present state.

No. 6291 is not exhibited. It is, however, part of the same series as Nos. 6284–90, above. For the history of these see No. 6290.

FLORENTINE SCHOOL
XV Century

6266 THE VIRGIN AND CHILD

Tempera (?) on panel; painted surface, 19½ × 13¼ (0·495 × 0·335).
Bequeathed by Lord Carmichael (d. 1920), with a life interest to his widow; entered the Collection in 1956.
The picture has been lent to the National Gallery of Scotland, where it is exhibited.

Jan FYT
1611–1661

Flemish School; worked in Antwerp.

6335   STILL LIFE WITH FRUIT AND GAME

Oil on canvas, 33⅝ × 45 (0·855 × 1·143).
Bequeathed by Claude Dickason Rotch, 1962.

Thomas GAINSBOROUGH
1727–1788

British School, born at Sudbury, Suffolk; worked in Ipswich, Bath and London.

6301   MR. AND MRS. ANDREWS

Oil on canvas, 27½ × 47 (0·698 × 1·194). Apparently in excellent condition.

The sitters are traditionally identified and the picture remained in their family presumably from the time of its delivery by the artist until it was sold by a descendant in 1960. The man is Robert Andrews (1726?–1806) of Auberies, near Bulmer, actually in Essex but close to Sudbury, the Suffolk birthplace of Gainsborough. He married 10 November 1748 at All Saints Church, Sudbury, Frances Mary Carter (ca. 1732–80). She was a daughter of Mr. and Mrs. William Carter, of whom Gainsborough also painted a group portrait.[1] The church in the background of No. 6301 has been identified as St. Peter's, Sudbury.

The picture does not seem to have been painted until some months after the marriage; to judge from the costume, the year is likely to have been 1750. Presumably it was painted in the early autumn, for the cornfield has been newly reaped, and Mr. Andrews has his gun, game-bag and dog beside him. The area in Mrs. Andrews' lap is the only unfinished part of the picture, and it seems quite conceivable that she was intended to be shown holding a pheasant shot by her husband.

Of all Gainsborough's early pictures, this one is recognised as his masterpiece. The landscape is perhaps the most beautiful yet painted by any English artist and it belongs with the sitters quite literally, for it is probably on their own land that they are portrayed. This is in effect a new type of English portrait, initiated by Gainsborough and here already reaching its quintessence, in which not just the sitter's appearance but something of his environment is portrayed. Very different from the allusive baroque portraiture of the 17th century, Gainsborough's early portraits record with an enchanted literalness (a blend of French and Dutch influences) truth to nature: solid, stolid English country gentlemen and their wives and, in this picture, a panorama of the countryside that had made them.

Perhaps the beauty and freshness of Gainsborough's literal statements were not appreciated; his later portraits invest the sitters with a more sketchy glamour. However, that type of picture also is supremely represented in the Exhibition by 'The Morning Walk' (see below).

Despite the fame of 'Mr. and Mrs. Andrews' today, the picture has been known for little more than half a century. Its existence was mentioned in 1904 by Armstrong in the 2nd edition of *Gainsborough and his Place in English Art*;[2] but only in 1927, when it was included in the Gainsborough bicentenary exhibition held at Ipswich, did the picture come before the public. It was then that Sir Charles Holmes, Director of the National Gallery, wrote to Mr. G. W. Andrews, the owner, to say that it was regarded as a picture of national importance. Since then it has been exhibited frequently and has often served abroad to represent the perhaps unexpected achievement of British painting. Sold by Mr. G. W. Andrews at Sotheby's on 23 March 1960, it was bought by Thos. Agnew and Sons, Ltd. From them it was acquired in May 1960, with the help of a Special Exchequer Grant and donations from the Pilgrim Trust, National Art-Collections Fund, Mr. and Mrs. W. W. Spooner and Associated Television Ltd.

EXHIBITED: 1927, Ipswich, *Bicentenary Memorial Exhibition of Thomas Gainsborough, R.A.*, No. 26; 1929, Brussels, *Peinture Anglaise*, No. 63; 1930, London, *Conversation Pieces*, No. 145; 1934, R.A., No. 265; Memorial Cat. No. 180; 1934, Manchester, *British Art*, No. 19; 1936, London, Sir Philip Sassoon's, *Gainsborough*, No. 93; 1936, Amsterdam, *English Art . . .*, No. 35; 1937, London, Country Life, No. 277; 1949, Lisbon-Madrid, British Council, *Pintura Británica*, No. 18; 1949, Scandinavian Countries, British Council, *British Paintings . . .*, No. 44; 1953, Paris, *Paysage Anglais . . .*, No. 43; 1953, Tate Gallery, *Thomas Gainsborough*, No. 5; 1955, Rotterdam, *English Landscape Painters*, No. 31.

NOTES: (1) The present whereabouts of the picture is unknown; it was sold by the Andrews family in 1920. An upright of much simpler composition than the present picture, it must date from about the same period or perhaps somewhat earlier. (2) Walter Armstrong, *op. cit.*, p. 257. See also Ellis Waterhouse, *Gainsborough*, 1958, No. 18; and, for an appreciation of the picture, Waterhouse, *Painting in Britain 1530–1790*, 1953, p. 184.

6209 THE MORNING WALK

Oil on canvas, 93 × 70½ (2·360 × 1·791). Cleaned on acquisition. Somewhat restored.[1]

The couple represented are William Hallett (1764–1842) and his wife Elizabeth, *née* Stephen (1763/4–1833). They were married 30 July 1785, and were painted at about that time. The portrait's present title 'The Morning Walk' may well be of comparatively recent origin. It is quite likely that it was originally known as 'The Promenade' (or some similar name). The *Morning Herald* of 30 March 1786 announced that the picture, finished a few months before, had *promenaded* from Gainsborough's gallery, where it was no longer on view.[2] The *Morning Herald* was edited by Gainsborough's friend the Reverend Bate Dudley, and often contained informed reviews of his recent work—the more useful in that Gainsborough had quarrelled with the Royal Academy in 1783 and thereafter exhibited only at his own home, Schomberg House, still standing in Pall Mall.

In 'The Morning Walk' Gainsborough reaches the perfection of his late style of portraiture. He had long been impatient with the business of portrait painting, but he was now an established successful artist—with barely three years to live when it was painted—and could make what he wished of a portrait commission. The result is this group of elegant informality, a fashionably dressed married couple strolling contentedly, with an elegant Spitz dog, in a landscape as feathery and silken as Mrs. Hallett's costume. The apparent lack of 'finish' in the picture (in contrast with the 'Dutch' handling of 'Mr. and Mrs. Andrews') is quite intentional. Gainsborough at this date used specially long-handled brushes to give an airy, sketch-like quality to his work. This results in a type of 'impressionism' foreign to 18th-century English painting but preluding a significant aspect of 19th-century art.

The year after Elizabeth Hallett's death the picture was offered for sale at Foster's (9 August 1834); but it was not sold, and at about the same date it was exhibited for sale at the Pall Mall Gallery of John Allnutt. It was nevertheless inherited apparently by the Halletts' daughter Lettice Elizabeth. She married a Hilliard, and the picture was lent by W. E. Hilliard to the British Institution in 1859 and to the International Exhibition at South Kensington in 1862. From the Hilliard collection it was sold 15 April 1884 to Agnew, who sold it eight days later to Sir Nathan Rothschild (created Lord Rothschild in 1885). It was purchased from Lord Rothschild in 1954, out of Grant-in-Aid and with the Temple-West Fund, with a contribution from the National Art-Collections Fund (Sir Robert Witt Fund).

EXHIBITED: 1859, British Institution; 1862, South Kensington Museum, International Exhibition; 1885, R.A., No. 195; 1936, Sir Philip Sassoon's, *Gainsborough*, No. 11; 1938, Paris, No. 52; 1953, Tate Gallery (Arts Council), *Gainsborough*, No. 50.

NOTES: (**1**) It was found to be somewhat rubbed by an earlier cleaning in the blue and black of William Hallett's costume, and there were a few fundamental damages. There was much overpainting to disguise the heavy craquelure in the shadows. (**2**) For the picture's history in detail see Martin Davies, National Gallery Catalogues, *The British School*, 1959, pp. 44–45.

COPY: According to information kindly given by a member of the Hilliard family in 1962, a copy was made in 1884 for the family and was at Cowley House, Uxbridge.

6242   GAINSBOROUGH DUPONT

Oil on canvas; 17½ × 14¼ (0·445 × 0·360), unfinished.
The sitter (*ca.* 1755–97) was Gainsborough's nephew, and himself a painter.
Bequeathed by Lady D'Abernon, 1954.

Style of GAINSBOROUGH

6281   LANDSCAPE

Oil on canvas, 24½ × 29½ (0·620 × 0·750).
Bequeathed by R. W. Lloyd, 1958.

Corrado GIAQUINTO
ca. 1695–1765

Italian School; worked in Rome, Naples and Madrid.

6229 THE CROWNING OF SPAIN(?)

Oil on canvas, 38 × 17 (0·965 × 0·432).
Bought out of the Waycott Fund in 1954.

Luca GIORDANO
1634/5–1705

Neapolitan School. Born in Naples, he was something of an infant prodigy thanks to the over-eagerness of his father, who was also a painter. He was influenced by the leading Italian Baroque painters, notably Pietro da Cortona, by Rubens and by the Venetians of the 16th century. He was a great decorative artist, whose work was in demand in Rome (cf. the picture below), Florence and Venice, as well as in Madrid, where he worked at the Spanish Court for ten years from 1692. He painted countless altarpieces, decorative pictures and some pastiches in the style of other painters. His comparatively light palette and his airy compositions herald the rococo style of the 18th century. He was indeed an important influence particularly on the Venetian decorative painters of the 18th century, for whom he was a prototype also in his journeyings.

6327 THE MARTYRDOM OF S. JANUARIUS

Oil on canvas, 42 × 31¾ (1·067 × 0·806). Apparently in good condition.

S. Januarius, Bishop of Benevento, was beheaded near Pozzuoli *ca.* 305. An Angel has flown down with the palm of martyrdom as the executioner draws his sword. Below on the left are the headless bodies of two of the Deacons and Lectors who suffered martyrdom at the same time.

S. Januarius is the patron saint of Naples, and the altarpiece for which this is the finished sketch or *modello* is in S. Spirito dei Napoletani in Rome. Rather more drama and vivacity may be claimed for the *modello*, which has several variations in composition from the large picture.[1] This must certainly have been painted before 1692, when Giordano went to Spain. Its presence in the church is not recorded apparently in late 17th-century guide-books; but the altarpiece probably dates from the decade of the 1680's. Both altarpiece and *modello* have all the characteristics of Giordano's mature style.

Nothing is known of the commissioning of the altarpiece; but it is conceivable that it is connected in some way with the jurist Cardinal de Luca, who came from southern Italy. He died in 1683 and his monument by Domenico Guidi is one of the few things of interest in S. Spirito dei Napoletani.

The picture was bought from Messrs. P. and D. Colnaghi in 1962 out of the Martin Colnaghi Fund.

EXHIBITED: April–May 1962, Colnaghi, *Paintings by Old Masters*.

NOTES: (**1**) The altarpiece was No. 264 in the '*Settecento a Roma*' Exhibition in Rome, 1959. It was cleaned for the occasion.

GIORGIONE
Active 1506; died 1510

Giorgio da Castelfranco. Venetian School. Born at Castelfranco Veneto; worked in Venice.

6307 SUNSET LANDSCAPE WITH S. ROCH(?), S. GEORGE AND S. ANTHONY ('Il Tramonto')

Oil on canvas, $28\frac{7}{8} \times 36$ (0·733 × 0·915). Cleaned on acquisition. Parts of the picture are a modern reconstruction; but a considerable majority of the total surface is in good and crisp condition.[1]

The interpretation of the subject has hitherto caused great difficulty. The suggestion first made—Anchises finding Aeneas in the Elysian fields[2]—is incompatible with the S. George group which was revealed subsequently, or with the figure of S. Anthony Abbot, identifiable by his pig, emerging here from the bank beneath him.[3] In any case this suggestion was evidently due to a wish to equate the picture with one of that subject mentioned by Marcantonio Michiel as the work of Giorgione. This was specified as a large picture, and such an identification would always have been improbable. In his life of Giorgione, Vasari mentions that his frescoes on the Fondaco dei Tedeschi in Venice were currently supposed to have no specific subject. Such may also be the case with one of his most famous surviving easel pictures, the 'Tempest', where no figure is readily identifiable. But the background figures in the '*Tramonto*' undoubtedly represent S. George and S. Anthony—the monster, or monsters, in the water being perhaps among those who tempted the latter—and it must therefore be assumed that the foreground figures are also specific and identifiable. At the same time, there can hardly be any *historical* relationship between the foreground figures, whoever they may be, and those in the background, since the latter do not relate historically to each other. The factor uniting the three groups would therefore be a thematic or doctrinal one. An element of this kind which S. George and S. Anthony undoubtedly share is popularity in the Veneto. Viewed in this light the young man seated in the foreground would most probably be S. Roch.[4] This saint, who was indeed greatly venerated in the Veneto, contracted the plague and an ulcer on his thigh. He thereupon left Piacenza and went out into the country, where a spring miraculously gushed to quench his thirst. His hunger was at first assuaged by the dog of one Gothardus, which brought him a loaf of bread every day. Later, the dog's owner, having followed the animal to the spot, himself took over the care of the sick man. In the present picture the younger (seated) man is shown with a short beard, as S. Roch normally is, and with a staff (on the ground in front of him), as is universal. A spring gushes from the rock near him, and the older man is evidently tending his left leg.

S. Roch was invoked against the plague. An outbreak of plague had occurred in Venice in 1504 (the next, and more, severe epidemic, in 1510, included Giorgione himself among its victims). If, as seems likely, the foreground figures in the 'Tramonto' are S. Roch and Gothardus the picture may well have been intended to commemorate the plague of 1504. Such a supposition would accord with stylistic factors. The 'Tramonto' seems a rather less developed work than the 'Tempest' and is therefore probably of slightly earlier date. The 'Tempest', though not itself dated, is usually associated with the Vienna portrait of a lady, which has an inscription on the back vouching for it as Giorgione's work and giving the date 1506. Some time about the year 1505 would therefore be a plausible dating for the 'Tramonto'.

To align three saints hieratically in a picture was a common thing in the Veneto. To dispose them within a landscape, as in the present picture, would have been a revolutionary novelty; but, as Giorgione was one of the most significant pioneers of landscape painting, such a solution of an old problem may now be seen as entirely characteristic of him.

In other ways too the 'Tramonto' may be regarded as the quintessence of the Giorgionesque. Many features in it were pointed out, at the time of the Venice exhibition and later, as closely comparable with others in two of Giorgione's most famous paintings, the 'Tempest' (Venice) and the 'Three Philosophers' (Vienna). A third work—a drawing of a young man seated in a landscape (Rotterdam)[5]—is comparable both in the relation of the main figure to the landscape and in the curiously attenuated legs of the youth in both cases. This feature recurs in a Giorgionesque engraving of a shepherd by Giulio Campagnola,[6] which may in fact be based directly on the 'Tramonto' since in addition to showing as the main figure a youth very similar, in reverse, to the younger of the two (? S. Roch) in the foreground of the 'Tramonto' it includes the head and shoulders of a bearded man like the other (? Gothardus) in the painting. A further engraving by Giulio Campagnola—the so-called 'Astrologer'[7]—bears the date 1509, and shows a monster comparable with the one in the 'Tramonto'. Yet another—called the 'Music Party'—shows a similar distant landscape.[8] These comparisons should suffice to justify the inclusion of the 'Tramonto' in the heart of the Giorgionesque repertory. That it is likely to be an original of the master and cannot be a copy emerges from the X-ray photographs, which reveal, among other things, fundamental changes made during painting in the buildings in the middle distance.

The main areas of damage and restoration are the bank and the stretch of water immediately under the S. George group; also much of the interior of the foliage of the tree on the left. There seems a possibility that the water originally contained further monsters comparable with the Bosch-like one seen emerging on the left; and there is therefore a remote chance that the damage sustained in this area may have been deliberately caused on account of the disquieting subject matter. In any case it is likely enough that Giorgione had some knowledge of the art of Hieronymus Bosch. Three pictures by Bosch are reported in Venice only eleven years after Giorgione's death and may very well have been there during his lifetime.[9] There is a further possibility of some influence from a northern artist, this time Dürer. Trees such as the one on the left of the ' *Tramonto* ', with roots visible on the outside of the rock, were a motive which occurs repeatedly in his engravings. One of these, of S. Jerome, may have influenced a painting of the subject by Lotto (dated 1506 and now in the Louvre) which shows a similar relation of landscape and figure to the ' *Tramonto* '.

The picture was discovered in 1933 in a neglected condition in an attic of the Villa Garzone at Ponte Casale in the Veneto. This had passed to the Donà Dalle Rose family from that of Michiel, and one member of the Michiel family, Marcantonio, had been one of the earliest writers on Giorgione's pictures, leaving a diary written a few years after his death. After its discovery the picture was lined, but only very summarily restored. It was then sold privately, before the auction of the Donà Dalle Rose collection. It was then more thoroughly cleaned and restored in detail. It was this cleaning which revealed the remains of the group of S. George and the dragon, which had not been visible before. The picture was exported in 1934 to England, where it remained unseen until it was exhibited in Venice in 1955. From the time of its discovery in 1933 until 1955 the picture was not accessible to study. At the exhibition it was received with acclaim; and indeed it may be described as the only major Giorgione discovery of this century.[10] After it was acquired by the Gallery it was cleaned and restored for the third time,[11] revealing the original paint of S. George's bright blue saddle cloth which had been concealed before but which can now be seen to constitute an important colour accent. It was bought in 1961 through Messrs. Colnaghi out of Grant-in-Aid, with contributions from the Temple-West, Champney and Florence Funds.

EXHIBITED: 1955, Venice, Doge's Palace, *Giorgione e i Giorgioneschi*, No. 30.

NOTES: (**1**) The picture was exhibited for some weeks in 1961 with a number of annotated photographs and a diagram and an X-ray print showing the exact extent of the damage. The diagram is reproduced in the *National Gallery Report* for January 1960–May 1962, monochrome Pl. 1. A photograph published in the *Illustrated London News* of 4 November 1933 of the picture as found gave an exaggerated impression of the damage. Owing to the use of raking light even the well preserved passages appear damaged. The only occasion before 1955 when a photograph of the picture subsequent to the second restoration (*i.e.* including the S. George group) was published was in R. Longhi's *Viatico per cinque secoli di pittura veneziana*, 1946 (Longhi had already referred briefly to the picture as by Giorgione in his *Officina Ferrarese*, 1934, p. 133). (**2**) By Giorgio Sangiorgi in *Rassegna Italiana*, November 1933. (**3**) It is not certain whether or not the figure of S. Anthony was visible before the second cleaning and restoration. (**4**) Suggestion originally made, tentatively, by Rosalie B. Green, Director of the Index of Christian Art, Princeton, in a private communication. Alternative, but less likely, interpretations of the foreground group would be the Good Samaritan or the miracle of the youth's leg performed by S. Anthony of Padua. (**5**) Reproduced in the catalogue of the 1955 Giorgione Exhibition at Venice, p. 290, No. 1. (**6**) Reproduced by G. M. Richter: *Giorgio da Castelfranco*, 1937, Pl. LXI, No. 104. (**7**) Reproduced Richter, *op cit.*, Pl. LVII, No. 101. (**8**) 1955 Exhibition catalogue, p. 299, not reproduced. (**9**) Marcantonio Michiel notes in his diary for 1521 three pictures by Bosch of fantastic subjects in the house in Venice of Cardinal Grimani. The latter had been made Cardinal in 1493 and had subsequently spent much of his time in Rome. (**10**) The picture, which had originally been exported from Italy as the work of Giulio Campagnola, was accepted as Giorgione by the committee of the 1955 exhibition which included Zampetti, De Logu, Fiocco, Longhi, Morassi, Moschini, Pallucchini and Lionello Venturi. (**11**) By Arthur Lucas, Chief Restorer. The earlier restorations had been by Vermeeren and by Dumler.

Francisco de GOYA
1746–1828

Spanish School; worked mainly in Madrid.

6322   THE DUKE OF WELLINGTON

Oil on panel, $23\frac{3}{4} \times 20\frac{1}{4}$ (0·603 × 0·515).

Purchased, with aid from the Wolfson Foundation and a Special Exchequer Grant, 1961. Stolen from the Gallery 21 August 1961. For a full account, see *The National Gallery, January 1960–May 1962*, pp. 30–38.

Jan van GOYEN
1596–1656

Dutch School; worked at Leiden, The Hague and elsewhere in Holland.

6154   A RIVER SCENE, WITH A HUT ON AN ISLAND

Oil on oak, $14\frac{9}{16} \times 13$ (0·370 × 0·330).

Signed on the boat in the left foreground: *VG* (linked).

Companion piece to No. 6155 below. Both were bequeathed by Mrs. Charles Carstairs in 1952; they entered the Collection in 1953.

6155   A RIVER SCENE, WITH FISHERMEN HAULING A NET

Oil on oak, $14\frac{9}{16} \times 13$ (0·370 × 0·330).

Signed on the boat in the left foreground: *VG* (linked).

EL GRECO
1541–1614

Domenikos Theotokopoulos, called *El Greco*. Spanish School; worked in Venice, Rome and Toledo.

6260   **THE ADORATION OF THE NAME OF JESUS**

Oil and tempera on pine, painted area (excluding the black border, which is painted up to the edge of the panel): $21\frac{5}{8} \times 13\frac{5}{16}$ (0·541 × 0·339). Cleaned on acquisition in 1955. In fair condition.[1]

Signed in Greek capitals: *DOMENIKOS* (*ME* in monogram) *THEOTOKO-POULOS* (*TO* and *OU* in monogram) *KRÈS 'EPOIA* (or *EI* in monogram), *i.e.*, 'Domenikos Theotokopoulos Cretan made [it]'.

This is almost certainly the *modello*[2] for the larger picture on canvas ($55\frac{1}{8} \times 43\frac{1}{4}$) in the Escorial. That it was painted after the big picture is very unlikely indeed in view of the spontaneity of the execution and the many *pentimenti*,[3] of which the most conspicuous is that by the left hand of the Angel pointing to the Holy Cipher. In all the lighter parts of the picture El Greco's under-drawing has become visible, but especially in the sky.

The Escorial picture is of different proportions, squarer and more generous in effect; there are few differences in composition: in the Escorial picture there is an additional figure in the foreground on the left and the shadow over the hinder part of the crowd is more definite, almost triangular in shape. All that follows in this text refers equally well to either picture, for, while El Greco worked out his own ideas—exceptionally complicated for him—in the *modello*, those of the art-historians concerning the iconography of the composition have been evolved from the study of the larger and hitherto more accessible picture.

As is customary a Cross surmounts the luminous monogram *IHS* (for *IHSUS*, the Greek spelling of Jesus). Kneeling in adoration beneath it to the left are the faithful, destined for Heaven, while to the right the damned are already in the mouth of Hell. Between them and behind, is Purgatory, where under the direction of two horsemen souls are being thrown from a bridge into the flames. On a luxurious carpet in the foreground, conspicuous in black, King Philip II of Spain kneels on two cushions.[4] Beside him, in the mantle of cloth of gold trimmed with ermine, is the Doge of Venice, and opposite them kneels the Pope in white alb, gold cope, stole and maniple, and red gloves.

The cult of the Adoration of the Name of Jesus had come to be associated with victories over the Infidel. In the Escorial picture the upright figure beyond the Doge holds a conspicuous sword. At least the foreground group of the faithful thus stands for the Church Militant, and the association of these three leaders points to the great naval victory of the Holy League over the Turks at Lepanto in 1571. The picture is evidently an allegory painted to celebrate it.[5] The fact that the Holy League was the only instance in which Spain was in alliance with the Holy See and Venice leaves little doubt concerning this hypothesis, even if the Pope here does not greatly resemble Pius V, who organised the League. The then Doge was Alvise I Mocenigo. It has been suggested that the figure to the Pope's left may be Cardinal Granvella and that to his right Cardinal Pacheco; both were prominent in the negotiations which created the League.[6] However, Philip II is the only one of the *dramatis personae* to be clearly identified by his portraits.[7] Pius had died in 1572, Mocenigo in 1577; and in any case it was presumably Philip II who commissioned the picture.

It has been suggested that it may have been commissioned in honour of Philip II's illegitimate brother Don Juan, who had the general command at Lepanto.

He died in 1578 and his body was brought from Flanders to the Escorial the following year. This suggestion is based in part on the supposition that one of the three figures in the left foreground of the Escorial picture is an idealized representation of Don Juan.[8] But none of these figures has sufficient character or attributes to be identifiable with any degree of certainty; moreover it is difficult to see why El Greco should have depicted only one of the three generals or why he should have chosen to idealize him and none of the other *dramatis personae* who were also dead; further, the absence of a third figure in the *modello*, while not ruling out this suggestion, would indicate that no particular significance was intended to be attached to this group. The Escorial picture is considered by more recent authorities to belong to El Greco's early years in Spain.[9] The *modello* is even more reminiscent of his Italian style.[10] El Greco was in Spain by 1577, and No. 6260 was probably one of the first pictures which he painted there.[11]

It is perhaps first mentioned in an undated list of pictures which belonged to D. Luis Méndez de Haro y Guzmán, Marqués del Carpio, and to his son D. Gaspar de Haro y Guzmán, Marqués de Eliche (d. 1687), who owned also 'The Rokeby Venus' by Velázquez (No. 2057).[12] From him it may have passed to D. Gaspar's daughter Doña Catalina, who married the 10th Duke of Alba in 1688; it probably remained in the possession of the Dukes of Alba until about 1802.[13] In the second quarter of the 19th century it was in the collection of King Louis-Philippe of France, and was exhibited in his Spanish Gallery in the Louvre 1838–48 (No. 264), the exhibition which first made Spanish painting known to the rest of Europe. After the death of the exiled King in 1850 in England, his pictures were sold by auction in London, 6–21 May 1853. Here No. 6260 was bought (2nd day, lot 112) for £31 by Graves for Sir William Stirling Maxwell (1818–78), author of *Annals of the Artists of Spain* (1st ed. 1848) and many other works, who was the first to make El Greco's work known in Britain. It was purchased from his grandson, Lt.-Colonel W. J. Stirling of Keir, in 1955 with the Waycott, Osborne and Campion Funds, but largely by remission of estate duty and with a Special Grant from the Exchequer.[14]

EXHIBITED: 1895–96, London, New Gallery, No. 173; 1928, Burlington Fine Arts Club; 1938, Spanish Art Gallery, No. 1; 1947, London, National Gallery, Arts Council, *Spanish Paintings*, No. 13; 1951, Edinburgh, National Gallery, Arts Council, No. 18.

NOTES: (1) The cloak and breeches of Philip II are largely repainted, and his cushion damaged. An analysis of the technique and support was made by Joyce Plesters, of the Scientific Department. Her note in the N.G. archives records that the blue of the garments of the man kneeling in the extreme left foreground and of the foremost Angel on the right in the sky has deteriorated by chemical action. Their colour was originally 'a clear, palish blue, to a grey mottled with a dirty yellow'. (2) *i.e.* small-scale painting done beforehand for approval. This view has been put forward by N. MacLaren, *An Exhibition of Spanish Paintings*, National Gallery, Arts Council, 1947, No. 13; J. Camón Aznar, *Dominico Greco*, 1950, p. 233 and No. 261; E. K. Waterhouse, *Spanish Paintings*, Edinburgh, Arts Council, 1951, No. 18; E. du Gué Trapier, *El Greco, Early Years at Toledo*, 1576–86, Hispanic Society of America, 1958, p. 20; H. Wethey, *El Greco and his School*, 1962, II, pp. 74–75, No. 116. (3) *i.e.* corrections by the artist which have resulted in his earlier effort becoming visible through the paint as this became transparent with time. M. B. Cossío, *El Greco*, Vol. I, 1908, pp. 334–35, describes No. 6260 as a repetition of the Escorial picture; A. L. Mayer, *El Greco*, 1926, No. 123a, as a later variant; A. Blunt (see note 5), as a 'version'. (**4**) Fr. Francisco de los Santos, *Descripción breve del Monasterio de S. Lorenzo el Real del Escorial*, 1657, is the first to describe the Escorial picture (see F. J. Sánchez Cantón, *Fuentes Literarias*, etc., Vol. II, 1933, pp. 287–88). He states that it was called '*La Gloria del Greco*' and proceeds to give a correct interpretation: '*De ordinario llaman à este Lienço, La Gloria del Greco, por vn pedaço de Gloria, que se vè en lo superior: mas tambien en lo inferior, se vèn à vn lado el Purgatorio, y el Infierno . . . y à otro la Iglesia Militante . . y. entre ellos Philipo Segundo . . . y en medio desta Gloria, está el nombre de IESUS, à quien adoran los Angeles humillados; y juntando esta adoracion, con la que en la tierra le están dando los hombres . . . podemos dezir al mirar al otro lado al Infierno, y Purgatorio, rendidos de le misma forma, que quiso significarnos acqui el Artifice, aquello de San Pablo:* "*In nomine Iesu omne genuefusflectatur, Coelestium, Terrestrium, et Infernorum*" [S. Paul's *Epistle to the Philippians*, II, v. 10]'. Blunt (see note 5) shows that El Greco's rendering of Purgatory is derived from 'various medieval legends of the type of Tundal's Vision'. It should be noted that two bridges appear in Tundal's vision, see *The Vision of Tundale: together with metrical Moralizations*, etc., 1843 ed., lines 408–40 and 570–700; also that los Santos states that Purgatory and Hell were '*rendidos de la misma forma*'. Camón Aznar, *op. cit.*, 1950, p. 223, suggests that Purgatory was situated beyond the shadow on the left of the larger picture. However, Cardinal Bellarmine stated: '. . . *est communis scholasticorum, purgatorium esse intra viscera terrae, inferno ipsi vicinum . . .*' (*De Purgatorio*, II, VI, in *Roberti Cardinalis Bellarmini. Opera Omnia*, ed. C. P. Lauriel, Vol. I, 1872, p. 395). The symbol of Hell had been already used by El Greco in his early triptych in Modena. Waterhouse, *loc. cit.*, calls it 'the open dragon's mouth' and Blunt, *op. cit.*, p. 59, states that the text of *Revelation* XIX, v. 20, is closely followed. But E. Mâle, *L'Art Religieux du XIIIᵉ Siècle en France*, 1923, p. 384, states that the mouth of Hell frequently found in Gothic art is the mouth of Leviathan; the words of *Job*, XLI, v. 20: 'Out of his nostrils goes forth smoke, as out of a seething pot or caldron' would seem applicable. In view of the examples cited by Mâle from the Gothic it seems unnecessary to see a conscious borrowing by El Greco here from Byzantine sources, as do R. Byron and D. Talbot Rice, *The Birth of Western Painting*, 1930, p. 191, who state: 'The mouth of the monster of Hell . . . is a familiar cliché in Athonite monasteries'. Blunt, *op cit.*, p. 62, suggests that the shadow to the left may be 'the shadow of the Almighty' (*Psalm* 91, v. 1) or the shadow of death under which man lives (*Psalm* 44, v. 19). A. Palomino describes the picture as '*una pintura pequeña del Juicio*' (see F. J. Sánchez Cantón, *Fuentes Literarias*, etc., Vol. IV, 1936, p. 88). No. 6260 was described in the Catalogue of Louis Philippe's Spanish Gallery as '*Le Jugement Dernier*'. It was D. Vicente Polero y Toledo, *Catalogo de los Cuadros del Real Monasterio de San Lorenzo*, 1857, p. 39, who first published the Escorial picture as '*El sueño de Felipe II*'. Cossío, *op. cit.*, No. 45, while retaining this title, suggested, p. 318, that it was a Gloria '*es decir, un cuadro funeral para Felipe II*'. H. Kehrer, *Spanische Kunst von Greco bis Goya*, 1926, p. 69, suggested that this composition was an allusion to the Holy Inquisition. In the same year A. L. Mayer, *op cit.*, No. 123, described it as an Adoration of the Name of Jesus by Philip II, in combination with angels and a Last Judgment. (**5**) Anthony Blunt, *Journal of the Warburg and Courtauld Institutes*, Vol. III, Nos. 1–2, 1939–40, pp. 58–69, discusses the significance of the Escorial picture at length and gives the most convincing explanation of its iconography. He states that General Stirling, a former owner of No. 6260, first suggested that the picture was essentially an Allegory of the Holy League. He discusses, pp. 66–67 and Pl. 10a, an engraving by Pieter Balten, late 16th century (perhaps after the altarpiece ascribed to Martin de Vos in the Chapel du Saint Nom de Jésus in S. Jacques, Antwerp), which is dependent in part on the same biblical text. This shows the Church Militant kneeling to the Holy Cipher, led by a Pope and an Emperor on the sole of whose shoe is a crescent, the symbol of Islam. An engraving of 1571 by Martin Rota shows Philip II and Mocenigo kneeling on a dragon—symbol of the Turk—before Pius V, and has a grouping similar to that of El Greco's composition. (**6**) Blunt, *op cit.*, p. 65 and footnotes 2 and 3, and Waterhouse, *loc. cit.* The identification with Cardinal Granvella is supported by comparison with Titian's portrait at Besançon. (**7**) The portrait here may perhaps be compared with that by Juan Pantoja de la Cruz in the Prado Museum (No. 1036). Byron and Talbot Rice, *op. cit.*, pp. 191–92, state that the pose is reminiscent of Byzantine models; Trapier, *op. cit.*, p. 21, suggests that El Greco may have been influenced 'by the small, black-clad figures in *cartas ejecutorias de hidalguía* (letters patent of nobility)'. (**8**) See Blunt, *op. cit.*, pp. 65 and 68. Wethey, *op. cit.*, II, pp. 74–75, brings forward in support of this theory a print entitled '*Città di Venetia*' in Giacomo Franco, *Habiti d'Huomini et Donne Venetiane*, part II, 1614 (see A. Vallentin, *El Greco* trans. A. Révai and R. Chancellor, 1954, p. 130 ff., note 1 and Pl. 23), which was discovered by Blunt. Here the three generals of the Holy League kneel behind their rulers. This would suggest that in the picture all three should be present, rather than two (Wethey) or one (Blunt). For a further doubt on this theory see Trapier, *op. cit.*, pp. 22–23. (**9**) Cossío. *op. cit.*, No. 45, suggested 1594–1604; but Mayer, *loc. cit.*, *ca.* 1579; L. Goldscheider, *El Greco*, 1938, Pl. 49, 'about 1580'. Wethey, *loc. cit.*, No. 117, *ca.* 1579. (**10**) Trapier, *op. cit.*, p. 20, points out a number of characteristics of El Greco's Italian manner in No. 6260; see also Camón Aznar, *op. cit.*, p. 229: he describes the Escorial picture as '*la muestra más acabada del arte del Greco en el transito de Roma a España . . . en su primer periodo toledano, en 1576–77*'. D. Talbot Rice in the *Listener*, 16 March 1961, p. 475, again exaggerates the Byzantine elements in the composition, Mayer, *loc. cit.*, draws attention to Dürer's 'Gloria' as a comparison. Blunt, *op. cit.*, p. 69, points out the possible influence of Correggio in the rendering of the Angels. A good example of the extent to which El Greco could quote the Italian masters is seen in the 'Christ driving the Traders from the Temple'. No. 1457 in the National Gallery (see N. MacLaren, *Catalogue of Spanish Paintings*, 1951, p. 13). (**11**) Mayer, *op. cit.*, No. 123a, dates No. 6260, 1580–82; MacLaren, *loc. cit.*, suggests a date "at the end of the 1570's and the beginning of the 1580's"; Camón Aznar, *op. cit.*, No. 261, proposes a date near 1576/7; Waterhouse, *loc. cit.*, agrees with the latter date, though he also thinks 1578 'probable'; Wethey, *loc. cit.*, No. 116, suggests *ca.* 1578. He suggests, *op. cit.*, Vol. I, p. 11, that the commission was given to El Greco during his stay in Madrid in 1577. (**12**) See A. M. de Barcia, *Catálogo de la Colección . . . del Duque de Berwick y de Alba*, 1911, pp. 245–46. (**13**) See Wethey, *op. cit.*, II, p. 55, and Waterhouse, *loc. cit.* (**14**) Announced by the Chancellor of the Exchequer, Mr. R. A. Butler, in the House of Commons, 25 October 1955. This was the first occasion on which a Special Grant was made by the Government on the recommendation of the Reviewing Committee on the Export of Works of Art. For the considerable controversy which was roused over the various issues involved, see the *National Gallery Report*, 1955–56, pp. 67–69.

Francesco GUARDI

1712–1793

Italian School; worked in Venice.

6156   VENICE: THE PUNTA DELLA DOGANA

Oil on canvas, $7\frac{3}{8} \times 9\frac{3}{8}$ (0·182 × 0·238).
Companion piece to No. 6157 below. Both were bequeathed by Mrs. Charles Carstairs in 1952; they entered the Collection in 1953.

6157   VENICE: THE GIUDECCA WITH THE ZITELLE

Oil on canvas, $7\frac{3}{8} \times 9\frac{3}{8}$ (0·187 × 0·238).
See No. 6156.

Henri-Joseph HARPIGNIES

1819–1916

French School; worked in Paris, at Saint-Privé (Yonne) and in Italy.

6325   UNE SOIRÉE D'AUTOMNE

Oil on canvas, $45\frac{3}{4} \times 62$ (1·162 × 1·575).
Signed and dated: *h. harpignies 94*.
Bequeathed by Pandeli Ralli, 1928 (cf. Daubigny, No. 6323 above).

Meyndert HOBBEMA
1638–1709

Dutch School; worked in Amsterdam.

6138 A VIEW OF THE HAARLEM LOCK AND THE HERRING-PACKERS' TOWER, AMSTERDAM

Oil on canvas, $30\frac{1}{4} \times 38\frac{5}{8}$ (0·77 × 0·98). Cleaned on acquisition. On the whole in good condition. There is slight wearing in a few places but the only damage of consequence is in the covers of the pulley blocks each side of the lock, the dark parts of which have almost disappeared.[1]

Signed near the stern of the boat in the foreground towards the left: *m hobb*(·)*ma* (very faint; the last three letters are barely visible in ordinary lighting).[2]

The Haarlem Lock (Haarlemmersluis) and the Herring-Packers' Tower (Haaringpakkerstoren) are here seen from the South-West. The view is taken from the West side of the Singel canal at its junction with the Brouwersgracht, the end of which is in the left foreground. In the centre is the Haarlem Lock, the reconstructed walls of which still stand; the lock is now blocked and the drawbridge replaced by a permanent one. In the left background can be seen the corner of the Haarlemmerdijk (now the Haarlemmerstraat). In the centre background are the masts of shipping in the former open harbour in the IJ. On the right, beyond the lock-keeper, is the beginning of the Nieuwendijk.

None of the buildings seen in the painting has survived. The Herring-Packers' Tower, originally the Holy Cross Tower (Heilige Kruistoren), stood detached at the water's edge on the corner of the Singel and the Buitenkant (now Prins Hendriks Kade). It was part of the town fortifications built at the end of the 15th century; its spire was added at the beginning of the 17th century. It took its later name from the adjoining herring-packery and its weather-vane was a herring (visible in the picture). The spire was replaced by a cupola in 1813 and the whole tower was pulled down in 1829.[3]

Miss van Eeghen[4] has demonstrated that this picture shows the view as it was before 1662 at the latest, and most probably before 1661. In 1662 the little low house on the corner of the Nieuwendijk (here only partly visible just above the two men working the lock gates) was replaced by a tall house with a necked gable. This later house, dated on the façade: *ANNO 1662*, can be seen in a painting of the same view by Jan Ekels the elder (dated 1767) in the Amsterdam Historical Museum.[5] At the end of 1660 or the beginning of 1661 the buildings of the New Fish Market were erected on the West bank of the Northern end of the Singel canal,[6] *i.e.* beyond the left side of the lock in the picture; there appears to be no sign of them here (it is unlikely that the low dark shape just beyond the left half of the lock in Hobbema's view has anything to do with the new market buildings, which remained on this spot until the second quarter of the 19th century).

Although the picture shows the view before the alterations of 1661–62 it does not necessarily follow that it was painted previously; it would not be out of keeping with the practice of 17th-century Dutch view-painters to paint from a drawing made years earlier, even if the scene had since changed. The problem of dating in the present case is complicated by the lack of knowledge of Hobbema's style prior to 1661–62, which is due to the absence of fully acceptable dated works. None is known before 1658.[7] The river landscape at Detroit is signed and apparently dated 1658; it is related in style to Ruisdael's earlier manner and, if it is by Hobbema, it must certainly have been painted much earlier than No. 6138, which is in a considerably more developed style. No absolutely certain works of 1659–1661 are known.[8] It is, therefore, not possible to exclude entirely the possibility that No. 6138 represents a phase of Hobbema's development before 1662. On the other hand there are many pictures by Hobbema dated from 1662 onwards and No. 6138 seems closer in handling to the works of the mid-sixties[9] than to those of the early 'sixties.[10] A date about 1665 must, therefore, be seriously considered.[11]

Hobbema painted several views of indentifiable places (e.g. two in the National Gallery) but this is the only true 'townscape' by him known to exist. There is no reason to suppose that the buildings here are not his work; they are handled in exactly the same manner as the cottages in his wooded landscapes.

It is perhaps worth noting that Hobbema, who apparently settled in Amsterdam some years before 1660,[12] was living by November 1668 in the Haarlemmerdijk, the corner of which appears in the picture.[13]

It has been suggested[14] that the present picture is identical with the 'view along the Singel towards the Haarlem Lock and the Herring-Packers' Tower' attributed to Jacob van Ruisdael in the sales of Catharina Backer, widow of Allard de la Court van der Voort, Leyden, 8 and 9 September 1766 (lot 163),[15] bought by Verbeek (320 guilders), and Jan Danser Nijman, Amsterdam, 16 and 17 August 1797 (lot 225),[16] bought by C. S. Roos (400 guilders). No. 6138 was certainly in the following sales:[17] Pieter de Smeth van Alphen sale, Amsterdam, 1 and 2 August 1810 (lot 41), bought by J. de Vries (bought in), 1,000 guilders; Henry Croese sale, Amsterdam, 18 September 1811 (lot 31), bought by de Vries (bought in), 600 guilders; sale of paintings from the Croese collection et al., Amsterdam, 20 July 1812 (lot 18), bought by Gruijter (455 guilders). It was in the [T. G. Campbell] sale, London, 25 June 1831 (lot 90), bought by Nieuwenhuys (213 gns.);[18] [C. J.] Nieuwenhuys sale, London, 10 and 11 May 1833 (lot 68),[19] bought by Reeve (bought in ?), 405 gns.[20] apparently also at one time in the possession of A. Brondgeest.[21] It was in the collection of Baron J. G. Verstolk van Soelen, The Hague, by 1834;[22] his whole collection was sold in 1846 to Thomas Baring, S. Jones Loyd, Humphrey St. John Mildmay and Chaplin,[23] the Hobbema being among those pictures which fell to Mildmay (who died in 1853). Lent by his son, Henry Bingham Mildmay, to the Royal Academy, 1876 (No. 149); H. B. Mildmay sale, London, 24 June 1893 (lot 23),[24] bought by

Dr. J. P. Richter (£2,310). By Autumn 1921 it was in the possession of A. J. Sulley, London,[25] who sold it in May 1923 to Alfred Mildmay (son of H. B. Mildmay),[26] from whom it passed to his sister, Miss Beatrice Mildmay, London. Beatrice Mildmay Bequest, 1953.

EXHIBITED: 1876, London, R.A., No. 149.

COPY: A copy is in the collection of Mevrouw P.E. 't Hooft-Spakler, Amsterdam.[27]

NOTES: (**1**) It has been suggested that the picture is not in a good state of preservation by I. H. van Eeghen in *Oud-Holland*, Vol. LXVIII, 1953, p. 126, note 13. Although the shadows of the covers of the pair of pulleys each side of the lock are almost entirely worn away, the damage elsewhere is negligible, being confined to light wearing of the contours of the trees and of the adjacent parts of the sky over earlier outlines of them; some of the figures are also thin. Otherwise the paint is well preserved, even the delicate rigging of the ships in the centre distance being intact. (**2**) The doubts expressed about the genuineness of the signature by Miss I. H. van Eeghen, *op. cit.*, p. 125, are groundless. The fact that it is not mentioned in the Mildmay 1893 sale catalogue is of no significance; this catalogue also omits mention of the signatures on lots 36, 71, 76, 86 and 88, all of which are in fact signed. It is worn and faint and could scarcely be seen before the picture was cleaned; this would account also for the misattribution of the picture in certain 19th-century sales. (**3**) For the Herring-Packers' Tower see *Zeven eeuwen Amsterdam*, edited by A. E. D'Ailly (1942 onwards), Vol. III, p. 138. A view of the tower from the West by Johannes Storck, dated 1687, was in an anonymous sale, London, 10 July 1953 (lot 112) and one from the East by Abraham Storck, also of 1687, was in the Lady Keppel sale, London, 28 November 1956 (lot 117). It appears with an open cupola in a water-colour drawing made in 1816 by Gerrit Lamberts (reproduced in *Zeven eeuwen Amsterdam*, Vol. III, p. 184) and in a painting of 1826 by Johannes Jelgerhuis in the Rijksmuseum, Amsterdam (1920 catalogue, No. 1306). (**4**) I. H. van Eeghen in *Oud-Holland*, Vol. LXVIII, 1953, pp. 120–26. (**5**) Signed and dated 1767. In an anonymous sale, Amsterdam, 30 November 1909 (lot 109); reproduced by van Eeghen, *op cit.*, p. 123. Documents in the Amsterdam city archives confirm that the later house was built in 1662 (see van Eeghen, *op. cit.*, p. 124). (**6**) The new fish market was built in 1661 according to the so-called third edition of M. Fokkens' *Beschrijvingh der wijdt-vermaarde Koop-stadt Amstelredam*, 1664, p. 771, but it may have been begun by the end of the previous year; the market stalls were already leased by 1 May 1661 (see van Eeghen, *op. cit.*, p. 124). (**7**) Two pictures have sometimes been said to be dated 1657: Hofstede de Groot Nos. 77 and 132. The former is, in fact, dated 1689; the latter, now in the National Gallery of Victoria, Melbourne, is certainly dated 1662. (**8**) There are no less than five landscapes dated 1659 ascribed to Hobbema: *A roadside cottage* (Staedel Institute, Frankfort; Hofstede de Groot No. 32); *A woody landscape* (Edinburgh University, formerly deposited in the National Gallery of Scotland; Hofstede de Groot No. 150); *A flat landscape with a river* (Grenoble Museum; Hofstede de Groot No. 257); *A road by a pool* (Six van Vromade sale of 10 July 1923, lot 118; reproduced in G. Broulhiet, *Meindert Hobbema*, 1938, No. 368; from the Mondel collection, Wiesbaden); *A cottage among trees* (exhibited at the Royal Academy, London, 1938, No. 251, lent by Mrs. H. T. Mills). One or two of these are later imitations and none is beyond dispute (a radiograph of the picture in Edinburgh shows it is painted over a still life which must be later than 1659. The information was kindly supplied by the Director, David Baxendall). (**9**) *E.g.* the *Watermill* of 1664 in the collection of H. E. ten Cate (Hofstede de Groot No. 86) and the *Wooded landscape with cottages* of 1665 (Hofstede de Groot Nos. 61c and 228c; exhibited at the Royal Academy, 1952–53, No. 344). (**10**) *E.g.*, *The old oak* of 1662 in the Melbourne Gallery (Hofstede de Groot No. 132) and the *Wooded landscape* of 1663 in the National Gallery, Washington (Hofstede de Groot No. 171). (**11**) Neil MacLaren, National Gallery Catalogues, *The Dutch School*, 1960, pp. 172–76. With slight changes due to the difference in format the present entry reproduces MacLaren's entry of 1960. W. Stechow in *The Art Quarterly*, XXII, 1959, pp. 3–18, accepts two landscapes dated 1659 and one of 1660 and reconstructs Hobbema's early period in a way which supports MacLaren's datings. (**12**) *Oud-Holland*, Vol. XXX, 1915, p. 194. (**13**) *Gazette des Beaux-Arts*, 1864, i, p. 222. (**14**) K. E. Simon, *Jacob van Ruisdael*, 1927, p. 73, and in *Zeitschrift für Kunstgeschichte*, 1940, p. 210. (**15**) '*J. Ruysdael. De Haarlemmer-sluis en Haaring-pakkerstoren te Amsterdam . . .*'; $29\frac{3}{4} \times 38$ *duim*.

(16) '*Jacob Ruysdael Een Gezicht, ziende langs de Cingel na de Haarlemmersluis en Haringpakkers-Tooren te Amsterdam; met verscheide stoffagie . . .*'; on canvas 29 × 38 *duim*. (17) Miss van Eeghen has suggested (*op cit.*, p. 125, note 5) that, as the National Gallery picture and the copy in the 't Hooft collection are of almost the same size, it is not always possible to say whether the items in the 19th-century sales mentioned refer to the original or the copy. In fact, however, the picture in the Croese sales of 1811 and 1812 is identified in the catalogues of those sales as lot 41 of the Smeth van Alphen sale; Smith, *Catalogue raisonné*, etc., Hobbema, No. 28, certainly knew the picture, then belonging to Baron Verstolk van Soelen; he identifies it with that of the Smeth van Alphen, T. G. Campbell and Nieuwenhuys sales. The Nieuwenhuys 1833 sale catalogue mentions that it came from the Smeth van Alphen sale. Subsidiary evidence that the picture in the sales mentioned was the original is provided by the prices paid. (The identity of the National Gallery picture with that in the Mildmay collection in the 19th century is proved by the Royal Academy 1876 label and Mildmay 1893 sale markings on the back.) (18) As 'Storck: View of one of the Towers and part of the City of Amsterdam, with figures'. Storck's name is deleted in the auctioneer's marked copy of the catalogue of this (anonymous) sale, which gives the same vendor, purchaser and price paid for this lot as Smith does (*loc. cit.*). (19) As by Hobbema and from the Smeth van Alphen sale. (20) The auctioneer's marked copy of the sale catalogue names Reeve as the purchaser of lot 68; according to Smith (*loc. cit.*) the lot was bought in (both give the same purchase price). (21) The lining canvas is inscribed in ink: *A. Brondgeest*. It is not known when the picture was in his possession but he is known to have bought a number of pictures for Baron Verstolk (such as P. Koninck No. 4251 in the Gallery). (22) C. J. Nieuwenhuys, *A Review of the Lives and Works of some of the most Eminent Painters*, 1834, p. 140. (23) See W. H. J. Weale and J. P. Richter, *Descriptive Catalogue of the Collection of . . . the Earl of Northbrook*, 1889, pp. ix–x and 199. (24) See the end of note 17. (25) Hofstede de Groot, *Catalogue raisonné of the works of the . . . Dutch Painters*, Hobbema, No. 3, MS. note in de Groot's own copy at the Rijksbureau voor Kunsthistorische Documentatie at The Hague; Hofstede de Groot, who saw the picture when in Sulley's possession, adds that Sulley bought it from the purchaser at the Mildmay sale [presumably not Richter who probably bought it for someone else]. (26) A copy of A. J. Sulley's receipt, kindly communicated by Messrs. Baring Bros., is in the National Gallery archives. (27) On canvas, 0·79 × 1·00. In an anonymous sale, Amsterdam, 30 November 1909 (lot 107) as by J. Beerstraten, bought by August Janssen, Amsterdam; after Jansen's death it came into the possession of J. Goudstikker, Amsterdam, who sold it in 1919 or 1920 to C. G. 't Hooft, Amsterdam (cf. van Eeghen, *op. cit.*, p. 123); Historical Exhibition, Amsterdam, 1925 (No. 420). Reproduced in the Amsterdam 30 November 1909 sale catalogue, and the Amsterdam 1925 exhibition catalogue. It agrees in detail with the original except for the weather-vane, which in the copy is a cock. Since the well-known herring weather-vane remained in position on the tower until the demolition of 1829 (it can be seen in Jelgerhuis's painting of 1826 mentioned in note 3) it is conceivable that this rather pedestrian copy may be 19th-century.

JOHN HOPPNER
1758(?)–1810

English School; worked in London.

6333   PORTRAIT OF SIR GEORGE BEAUMONT

Oil on canvas, 30½ × 25⅛ (0·775 × 0·639).

Sir George Beaumont (1753–1827) gave his collection of pictures to the National Gallery. His promise to do this if a Gallery were founded was instrumental in the foundation of the Gallery by the purchase of the Angerstein collection in 1824.

Bequeathed by Claude Dickason Rotch with other pictures, 1962.

Karel du JARDIN
1621/2(?)–1678

Dutch School; worked at The Hague, Amsterdam and in Italy.

6296   THE CONVERSION OF S. PAUL

Oil on canvas, 73½ × 53 (1·865 × 1·345).
Signed and dated, bottom left: *K· DU· IARDIN. fe/1662* (the N reversed).
Presented by Mrs. Violet Van der Elst in 1959.

Cornelius JOHNSON
1593–1661

British and Dutch Schools; worked in London, Middelburg and Utrecht.

6280   PORTRAIT OF A LADY

Oil on canvas, 39¼ × 32 (1·000 × 0·810).
Signed and dated: *Cornelius Jonson/van Ceulen,/fecit/1655*.
Bequeathed by R. W. Lloyd, 1958.

Jacob JORDAENS
1593–1678

Flemish School. Baptised in Notre Dame, Antwerp, 20 May 1593, he was already apprenticed to Adam van Noort in 1607. In 1616 he married van Noort's eldest daughter, Catherine. His father-in-law, wife and children were used frequently as models. By 1649, perhaps, he already had leanings towards Calvinism, and from 1674 Protestant services took place in his house. He died 18 October 1678, and was buried at Putte in Dutch Brabant.

Jordaens lived and worked in Antwerp. After six years' membership, he was made a deacon of the Guild of S. Luke there in 1621. His first generally known signed and dated work is 'The Adoration of the Shepherds' of 1616 in the Metropolitan Museum, though a 'Diana and her Nymphs' of 1614 is also recorded. His first major commission seems to have been the 'Martyrdom of S. Apollonia' for S. Augustine, Antwerp, in 1628. He was of course much influenced by Rubens, with whom he collaborated on at least two occasions. However, his manner always remained distinctive. Towards the end of Rubens' life, Jordaens began to come into his own, and it might be said that Rubens' mantle passed to him. It is in the 'forties that the number of signed and dated works increase and that many versions of the same composition were produced by his studio. His output was large and variable in quality. He was copied in his own lifetime, and with his growing popularity studio participation obviously increased. A feature of Jordaens' distinctive manner is a certain coarseness in technique, which increased with old age.

6293 PORTRAIT OF A MAN AND HIS WIFE

Oil on canvas, 84 × 74 (2·125 × 1·880). Cleaned on acquisition. In fair condition.[1]

The rich but sober costume is of about 1630.[2] The man stands, wearing an elaborate red sash trimmed with gold lace, a sword, slung from a baldrick, and a dagger; he holds a long staff or wand[3] to which the seated woman seems to point. These are almost certainly the insignia of the captain or some other high officer in a civic guard or militia company, such as are recorded in the famous groups of officers by Hals at Haarlem or in Rembrandt's 'Night Watch' with Captain Frans Banning Cocq and his company in Amsterdam. Above the carved console over the officer's right shoulder is a coat of arms. This is somewhat damaged and discoloured but would seem to be contemporary with the rest of the picture. It therefore provides the chief evidence concerning the identity of the sitters. The arms correspond with those of the van Surpele family of Diest in South Brabant: *de vair à la fasce de gueules chargées de trois martels d'or posés en bande rangés en fasce*.[4] The *martels* are represented the wrong way round,[5] but this inexactitude is probably not significant.

The arms were thus identified in 1888–89 by Hymans.[6] Strong[7] then proposed the 'Portraits of the Burgomaster of Diest and his Wife'; but this identification was rejected by Buschmann[8] and by Fierens-Gevaert.[9] Fierens-Gevaert, however, named in effect[10] the member of the van Surpele family whose career Strong had outlined, stating that the sitters were '*Godefroid-Jean van Surpele, pensionnaire de Diest et sa femme, Marie Duynau*'. The Abbé Polydore Daniels[11] then proposed the *pensionnaire*'s parents, Jan van Surpele and Marie van Horne. Both these candidates are rejected by van Puyvelde[12] as too young for the date of the picture. He places this about 1630, and this indeed conforms with the style of the dress.

The man is therefore probably Govaert[13] van Surpele (1593–1674), who was *échevin* of Diest in 1629 and three times its burgomaster: 1634–35, 1649–50 and 1651–52. He was *Président de la loi* in 1636–37.[14] This suggestion rests on the supposition that the man appears to be in his late thirties. Govaert married twice: first, in 1614, Catherina Cools, who died 11 September 1629; second Catherina Coninckx, who died 11 July 1639.[15] Since the date of the second marriage is unknown as yet, the identity of the wife is uncertain, even if the man is correctly identified as Govaert van Surpele. This must be considered as a suggestion until it can be shown that about 1630 Govaert van Surpele was captain or held some other high rank in a militia company or civic guard.

Throughout the greater part of the 18th and 19th centuries the sitters were believed to be members of the House of Orange.[16] It may well have been this belief that led to the importation of the picture. It is apparently first recorded in 1743, when it was in the sale of Thomas Scawen, in London.[17] Thomas was heir of his uncle Sir William Scawen, who 'died vastly rich' in 1722, and who 'had ventured almost his whole property in the cause of William III'. Legend records a visit by him to William III during the siege of Namur. Thomas Scawen inherited land from his uncle at Carshalton, where he planned a magnificent house which was never built.[18]

In the same year, 1743, the picture was noted by Vertue[19] at Devonshire House, the new London residence of the Dukes of Devonshire. It remained at Devonshire House[20] until this was demolished in 1924, when it was removed with other pictures to 32 Carlton House Terrace. During or after the war of 1939–45 it was removed to Chatsworth, Derbyshire. The picture was acquired from the 11th Duke of Devonshire in 1958 in part payment of estate duty, under the terms of the Finance Act, 1956.

DRAWING: Black and red chalk on paper, 0·292 × 0·388, on the market in Holland in August 1959. Photograph in the Gallery archives. This is probably a studio copy. The coat of arms is absent and other features show that it was made some time before the picture was completed in its present form: the figures themselves appear to be set further apart; the balustrade is lower to the right, and there are buildings in the landscape. Above all, the drawing repeats only that part of the composition which is comprised by the two horizontal seams in the canvas, with the figures in three-quarter length. This suggests that the painting *may* have been begun on that scale.

ENGRAVING: Mezzotint by J. van Rymsdyck 1767, see note 16.

EXHIBITED: 1837, London, British Institution, No. 143; 1895, Royal Academy, No. 122; 1905, Antwerp, *Jordaens*, No. 75; 1906, Guildhall, *Works of Flemish and modern Belgian Painters*, No. 88; 1910, R.A., No. 121; 1927, R.A., No. 159; 1938, R.A., No. 38; 1948, London, Agnew's, *Devonshire Collection*, No. 27.

NOTES: (**1**) The black areas of the costume, particularly that of the woman, are worn and re-touched. There are many *pentimenti*, some visible, others disclosed by infra-red photography. The canvas is made up out of six pieces. See above under DRAWING. (**2**) Note by Stella Mary Pearce in the Gallery archives. (**3**) M. Rooses and F. Reber, *Geschichte der Malerschule Antwerpens*, 1889, p. 366, describe the staff as a '*Commandoftab*'. The Abbé Polydore Daniels in the article mentioned in note 11 describes it as '*un bâton d'échevin*'—a sheriff's wand. (**4**) See Philippe d'Arschot and Gilbert van Linden, *Diest Inventaire des Peintures*, 1958, Section II, No. 9, p. 25 and note 1. (**5**) A description and drawing of the coat of arms was also kindly provided by Dr. J. Verbeemen. The vairs are described as azure; they now appear black but traces of light blue can be made out in the centre vair in the lower half of the shield. (**6**) See the entry for Jordaens in the *Biographie Nationale*, 1888–89, Vol. 10, p. 530. (**7**) S. A. Strong, *The Masterpieces in the Duke of Devonshire's Collection of Pictures*, 1901, p. 16 and Pl. 19. (**8**) P. Buschmann, Jr., *Jacques Jordaens*, 1905, Pl. xxiv and p. 103. He wrongly describes the van Surpele as '*une famille patricienne anversoise*' (**9**) H. Fierens-Gevaert, *Jordaens* 1905, p. 108. (**10**) Fierens-Gevaert, *loc. cit.* (**11**) Abbé Polydore Daniels, '*Apropos d'un tableau de Jordaens*', in *Bulletin de l'Academie Royale d'Archéologie de Belgique*', 1906, Vol. I, p. 212 *et seq.* He dates the picture 1666–70, and argues that, as Godefroid-Jean was born in 1650 and Anne-Marie Duynau in 1648, they could not have been its subject. Jan van Surpele lived 1618–76; his wife Marie was born in 1626. (**12**) L. van Puyvelde, *Jordaens*, 1953, pp. 126–27. (**13**) '*Govaert van Surpele Borgemester Jans sone en Catharina Cools conjuges 1672*' is the legend engraved on copper on the third column to the right of a balustrade round the main altar of S. Sulpice, Diest. This spelling of the family name, which appears with many variations in contemporary documents and in subsequent literature, has been adopted here throughout. (**14**) Information very kindly provided by G. van der Linden, archivist of Diest, who has given much appreciated help. His letter is in the Gallery archives. J.-Th. de Raadt, *Sceaux Armoriés des Pays Bas et des Pays Avoisinats*, 4 vols., 1893–1904, Vol. 3, p. 502 *et seq.*, gives a less elaborate description of the van Surpele arms and the dates of Govaert. (**15**) The dates of his death and of his two wives are taken from a description in the Diest archives by Monsieur le Chevalier van

Zurpele de Reynrode of the inscription on Govaert's tombstone in S. Sulpice at Diest. The inscription itself is now worn away. (**16**) 'The first Prince and Princess of Orange' is the title in the sale of Thomas Scawen, Cock's, London, 25-26 January (2nd day) 1743, lot 49, sold for £117. 'Frederick Henry and Emilia van Solms, Prince and Princess of Orange' is the title of Rymsdyck's mezzotint of 1767. (**17**) For details of the sale, see note 16. Thomas Scawen (died 1774) was son of Sir Thomas Scawen (died 1730), citizen and alderman of London, see Le Neve, *Pedigree of the Knights*, Harleian Society, Vol. 8, p. 441. He was M.P. for Surrey 1736, and married Tryphena, daughter of Lady Russell by her second marriage. (**18**) O. Manning and W. Bray, *The History and Antiquities of the County of Surrey*, Vol. II, 1809, pp. 510–11. (**19**) *Vertue's Notebook*, Walpole Society, Vol XXVI, 1937–38, p. 23: 'at the Duke of Devonshires new built house a great and noble collection of pictures . . . the great picture of the Prince of Orange & princes'. (**20**) J. D. Passavant, *Kunstreise durch England und Belgien*, etc., 1833, p. 71; Waagen, *Treasures of Art in Great Britain*, 1854, Vol. II, p. 94.

Laurent de LA HIRE
1606–1656

French School. Born in Paris, 27 February 1606, son of the painter Etienne de la Hire, under whom he studied mannerist decorative work. He did not visit Italy, but he was influenced by Italian art perhaps through Vouet (*q.v.*) and by Italian pictures in Paris. Later he felt the influence of Poussin's earlier work; and also Claude's, as is apparent in his treatment of landscape. He was employed on altarpieces for Parisian churches and decorative pictures, tapestry designs, etc. His figure paintings aim at a classical style (cf. the picture below), though he was not unaffected also by Flemish art. Died in Paris, 28 December 1656.

6329 ALLEGORICAL FIGURE OF GRAMMAR

Oil on canvas, $40\frac{1}{2} \times 44\frac{1}{2}$ (1·029 × 1·130). Apparently rubbed and retouched in parts, especially the head.

Signed and dated, bottom left: *L DE LA HIRE· in · · X · F 1650*, and inscribed: *VOX LITERATA ET ARTICVLATA /DEBITO MODO* (in reverse)/ *PRONVNCIATA*.

Bequeathed by Francis Falconer Madan with other pictures, 1962.

VERSION: Baltimore, Maryland, Walters Art Gallery, an apparently identical version on a canvas of the same dimensions; it is similarly inscribed and dated.

Pieter LASTMAN
1583–1633

Dutch School. Worked in Rome and Amsterdam.

6272 JUNO DISCOVERING JUPITER WITH IO

Oil on oak, $21\frac{3}{8} \times 30\frac{5}{8}$ (0·543 × 0·778). Cleaned on acquisition. In excellent condition.

Signed and dated at the top on the right: *Pietro Laftman/fecit A⁰ 1618*.

There are divers versions of the story of Io. The account best known in later times is that in Ovid's *Metamorphoses* (book I, 583 ff.). Io, daughter of Inachus, was seduced by Jupiter. Juno, looking down from the sky, saw the dark cloud he had spread to entrap Io and descended to earth to look for him. Jupiter, hoping to deceive her, had turned Io into a beautiful heifer but Juno made him give it to her and put it in the charge of Argus the hundred-eyed. At the orders of Jupiter, Mercury lulled Argus to sleep and killed him. Juno then caused Io to wander into Egypt; finally, however, she let Jupiter change her back into human form.

In verses 612–616 Ovid describes how Juno, having discovered Jupiter with the heifer, pretends not to know that the latter is Io and asks where it comes from and to whom it belongs; Jupiter says it was born of the earth, whereupon Juno asks for it as a gift. The gestures and expressions of the principal actors in Lastman's picture, especially Juno's, fit these lines so well that it is tempting to suppose the painter had Ovid's text in mind. On the other hand the two secondary figures do not occur in Ovid. The winged child is obviously Love; the other figure is certainly Deceit (the mask and the fox's skin are among Deceit's most usual emblems). Lastman may merely have introduced these allegorical figures as appropriate to the action but it is at least equally likely that he was following some contemporary poem or play.

After the death of Argus, Juno took his eyes to decorate the tail of the peacock; Lastman rightly shows the birds here without the 'eyes'.[1]

The picture was in an anonymous sale at Christie's, 3 May 1957, lot 152, 'Mercury and Argus with Juno'. It was presented in the following month by Julius Weitzner.

NOTE: (**1**) See Neil MacLaren, National Gallery Catalogues, *The Dutch School*, 1960, pp. 216–17.

LOUIS LE NAIN
ca. 1593–1648

French School. Born at Laon, like his elder brother, Antoine, and his younger, Mathieu. Louis and Mathieu followed Antoine to Paris in 1630. According to tradition, the three brothers collaborated on pictures, and this seems to have been the case at least with the two younger. The few signatures on pictures read merely '*Le Nain*', and the few documentary sources are of little assistance in distinguishing the work of any of the three. The style of Louis Le Nain, however, appears distinctive in many pictures, and he stands head and shoulders above his brothers. In the 18th century writers called him '*Le Romain*', which suggests a tradition that he visited Rome. It has been pointed out that he need not have gone to Rome to meet Pieter van Laer (*Bamboccio* to the Italians), the Dutchman who seems to have influenced his peasant scenes; van Laer passed through Paris and Louis could have visited his native Haarlem. What, however, distinguishes Louis from his brothers is the larger scale of his compositions and their more classical quality, even when they represent peasant life.

All three brothers worked in Paris and became members of the Académie Royale at its foundation in 1648. Both Antoine and Louis, however, died in that year.

6331 THE ADORATION OF THE SHEPHERDS

Oil on canvas, $43\frac{1}{8} \times 54\frac{3}{8}$ (1·095 × 1·374). Cleaned on acquisition; in excellent condition.

This picture was until its acquisition unpublished and quite unknown, at least as the work of Louis Le Nain. Its discovery in 1962 has added considerably to our knowledge of his work and capabilities. Probably since the 19th century it had been supposed to be Italian work, and its frame bore an old attribution to Luca Giordano. There are, indeed, Italianate elements in the picture, and these were emphasised by the heavy yellow-brown varnish which covered it at the time of its acquisition. Cleaning has revealed the subtlety and individuality of the colouring—notably on the robes of the two angels—and the strange sub-aqueous tonality that is a typical feature of Louis' paintings.

No. 6331 perhaps offers further evidence that he visited Rome. But it has to be remembered that some Italian 17th-century artists had been in France and exercised influence there, among them Orazio Gentileschi. The Virgin here seems to show traces of Orazio's style.

The picture does not suggest a work of collaboration, though Louis and Mathieu Le Nain did collaborate together. Religious pictures by them are in any case not common, and the present picture can reasonably be claimed to be the work of Louis Le Nain alone. Early inventories and sales attribute many pictures of 'The Nativity' and 'Adoration of the Shepherds' simply to the Le Nain; but as far as can be checked none of the pictures mentioned accords with No. 6331 in size. Among treatments of the subject by or ascribed to the Le Nain may be mentioned an upright picture in the Louvre now given to Mathieu and very different in handling from this picture. About 1640 seems a likely date for No. 6331.

It is believed to have been acquired by a Duke of Norfolk in the last century. It was purchased from the 16th Duke through Oscar Johnson in 1962 out of the Annual Grant-in-Aid.

LEONARDO DA VINCI

1452–1519

Italian School; worked at Florence, Milan and Rome, and in France.

6337 CARTOON: THE VIRGIN AND CHILD WITH S. ANNE AND S. JOHN THE BAPTIST

Black chalk heightened with white; on sheets of reddish-buff paper stuck together and now attached to canvas, $55\frac{3}{4} \times 41$ (1·415 × 1·04). The paper was probably tinted in the artist's studio. It has a good many tears and some substantial holes, over some of which (at the time of writing) there are clumsy retouchings. The drawing is rubbed in places, especially on Christ's body and the Virgin's right arm; but elsewhere many of the important parts are in very fresh condition for a cartoon. A good deal of the white is questionable.[1]

It is of varying degrees of finish; for instance, the feet of the Virgin and S. Anne, S. Anne's pointing hand and the rocky landscape at the top on the right are only sketched in. A cartoon (from the Italian *cartone*, large paper) is a guide for the painting of a picture. It was usually intended for application to the surface about to be painted, so that the outlines could be pricked through it on to this to provide direction for the outlines of the painting; but No. 6337 has not been pricked.[2]

The subject is a combination of two traditional themes: one the Virgin and Child with S. Anne, the other the Virgin and Child with the infant S. John the Baptist. The Virgin here sits on the lap of her mother, S. Anne;[3] there are various earlier examples of this pictorial symbolism, one that Leonardo is likely to have known being a sculpture in wood claimed to be from the altar of S. Anne in Orsanmichele, Florence.[4] In No. 6337, Leonardo has drawn S. Anne pointing upward with her left hand to Heaven. The theme of the Virgin and Child with the infant S. John is apparently of more recent, Florentine origin; it may not date from before about 1460, but it quickly became popular. The combination of the two themes may well be of Leonardo's invention; it is not known what circumstances occasioned it.

There are indeed no records of No. 6337 during Leonardo's life-time; it was in the possession of the Royal Academy for nearly 200 years until 1962, but its earlier history, as will be explained later, is not established with certainty. There are, on the other hand, various contemporary or ancient records of Leonardo's treating the subject of 'The Virgin and Child with S. Anne'.

The earliest known dated reference is in a letter of 3 April 1501 from Florence, written by Fra Pietro da Novellara.[5] He describes a cartoon, saying that this was the only work of art known to have been carried out by Leonardo since his arrival in Florence (where he had been for a year or so); the fairly detailed description does not suit the present drawing—in particular, the Florentine cartoon included a lamb, but it seems clear that it did not include S. John the Baptist. It should not be doubted that Fra Pietro is in the main exact; admittedly, he seems not to have seen Leonardo when he wrote,[6] but this does not mean that he had not seen the cartoon, and even if he had not, he must have had detailed information about it to write as he did.

Fra Pietro's record of the Florentine cartoon is of 1501. In 1550 was issued the first edition of Vasari's *Lives of the Painters*. Vasari[7] writes of a cartoon of the subject, which, he says, had been on public view in Florence for a short time, exciting much enthusiasm; it is not difficult to believe the truth of this, and identify Vasari's cartoon with Fra Pietro's. But Vasari's description seems obviously of far less authority than Fra Pietro's. It is, indeed, notably less precise;

but Vasari does say (for what it is worth) that the cartoon included both S. John and a lamb.[8]

This cartoon is said to have been taken to France,[9] but is not known now to exist. In France there was certainly a picture of the subject, recorded in Leonardo's studio in 1517;[10] the record is slight. It is usually, and reasonably, supposed to be identical with the well-known picture in the Louvre, which is considered to be unfinished, and to have been painted some years after 1501.[11]

No. 6337 is usually believed to be earlier than the Florentine cartoon and the picture in the Louvre; there appear to be good reasons for this view.[12]

The composition of the picture[13] seems clearly a maturer invention than the composition here.

The iconography of No. 6337 seems difficult to place anywhere in the series except first. Concerning the iconography of the missing Florentine cartoon, we have Fra Pietro's valuable comments. He says that there the Infant Christ was embracing a lamb, symbol of the Passion; the Virgin was trying to restrain Him from the Sacrifice, and S. Anne, who might stand for the Church, was restraining the Virgin, as if to indicate to her that the Passion was Destiny not to be altered. It should not be doubted that thoughts of this kind were in Leonardo's mind when he composed the Florentine cartoon;[14] indeed, Gerolamo Casio says much the same as Fra Pietro about what he calls a picture by Leonardo of the subject,[15] though it may be that his interpretation is not independent of Fra Pietro.[16] Further, it seems clear that this iconography, except for the part played by S. Anne, is preserved in the picture in the Louvre. But in the National Gallery cartoon the iconography is formed, as has been noted, of a combination of two traditional themes and seems clearly less evolved. True, the presence of S. John in No. 6337 recalls the Divine Mission of Christ; yet it may be that the only motif here apt to call forth iconographical comments in the style of Fra Pietro's is the hand of S. Anne pointing upwards to Heaven. It is to be remarked that, while S. Anne seems in the missing Florentine cartoon to have indicated the Destiny of Christ, she does not in the picture in the Louvre;[17] and the picture is presumed to be later. On iconographical grounds, then, it would seem that the National Gallery cartoon was first, mostly traditional but with reference to the theme of Salvation in S. Anne's gesture; this, differently expressed, seems to have been included in the Florentine cartoon, but with much new symbolism of the Passion in the Virgin, the Child and the lamb; and finally, in the picture in the Louvre, the iconographical additions of the Florentine cartoon seem to be preserved, but S. Anne no longer testifies by gesture or action to the Will of God.

On grounds of costume, a date in the mid-1490's is favoured for the National Gallery cartoon.[18]

Such a dating would place No. 6337 in the later part of Leonardo's first Milanese period. There is indeed evidence that it was known in Milan in the 16th century, particularly in a derivation from it in the Ambrosiana (already mentioned in note 2), by Bernardino Luini, and perhaps of *ca.* 1530; as will be recorded more fully presently, it may have belonged to Bernardino's son, Aurelio Luini. This does not prove that it was drawn in Milan, nor that it stayed continuously there, and would be of no weight against clear evidence that it was drawn in Florence. Yet the evidence that it was drawn, or even known in Florence in the first years of the 16th century seems to be slight. A drawing by Michelangelo at Oxford (see further under VERSIONS), held to be of that time, is sometimes brought forward in this connection. The drawing shows the Virgin and Child with S. Anne, and Michelangelo may well have been inspired by Leonardo's success with the subject in his Florentine cartoon; but it shows little connection with No. 6337, except (it seems) in the disposition of the Virgin's legs. The influence of the same part of the National Gallery cartoon is claimed also for Raphael's 'Madonna di Foligno' in the Vatican Gallery, held to have been painted after Raphael had left Florence, in Rome ca. 1511/12. More than this would be needed adequately to support the view that No. 6337 was drawn in Florence.

There is the further matter of Leonardo's own drawings (as distinct from cartoons) of the subject. Three compositional studies have survived, in the British Museum, in the Louvre and at Venice, accepted by Popham as connected with the National Gallery cartoon;[19] there are also some links with the composition of the picture in the Louvre. These drawings have been several times analysed for the evolution of the design;[20] they will not be discussed in this entry, since it seems that nothing definite for the dating of No. 6337 can be deduced from them.[21]

It is claimed by Cardinal Federico Borromeo that in his time there existed a Christ in clay, connected with the Christ in No. 6337.[22] Lomazzo[23] records a clay head of Christ; Clark thinks that Lomazzo's record is associable with two drawings at Windsor, which are unconnected with No. 6337.[24]

The attribution of No. 6337 to Leonardo is not usually doubted, and seems indeed unworthy of doubt. Popham[25] has written: 'Here we have the inestimable benefit of the authentic touch and of all the elements, except colour, which go to make up Leonardo's charm.' Berenson,[26] clearly making no reservations whatever about the attribution, wrote this appreciation: 'One will scarcely find draped figures conceived in a more plastic fashion, unless one travels back through the centuries to those female figures that once sat together in the pediment of the Parthenon. In Italian art we shall discover nowhere else a modelling at once so firm and so subtle, so delicate and so large as that of the Virgin's head and bust here. We should look in vain, also, for draperies which, while revealing to perfection the form and movement of the parts they cover, are yet treated so unacademically, are yet so much actual clothing that you can think away'. Nevertheless, some doubts concerning the authenticity have been expressed. Suida[27] thought No. 6337 not entirely autograph; in 1898, at the time of the Milanese Exhibition at the Burlington Fine Arts Club in London, the idea was current that it was executed by Cesare da Sesto;[28] because of Luini's related picture in the Ambrosiana (see under VERSIONS), the possibility that the cartoon is Luini's work was aired by Beltrami.[29]

The cartoon was the occasion of psychoanalysis by Freud,[30] and Sir Kenneth Clark has contributed further to interpretation along such lines.[31]

As to its history, it may be identical with a cartoon that Lomazzo says had been in France, but in his time belonged to Aurelio Luini (died 1593) at Milan. His description is not sufficient to identify it;[32] yet the picture in the Ambrosiana, which derives from the cartoon and is accepted as the work of Aurelio's father, Bernardino Luini,[33] may be thought to provide some confirmation of the identity. Writing of this picture by Luini, Cardinal Federico Borromeo (*Musaeum*, 1625, p. 21) appears to show knowledge of the existence of a cartoon corresponding with No. 6337, by Leonardo ('*cum exquisitissime delineasset opus*'). By that time No. 6337 may have belonged to the Milanese collector Galeazzo Arconati, who is known to have acquired some of his Leonardiana from the sculptor Pompeo Leoni (died 1608). In 1639 Galeazzo offered one of two works by Leonardo to Cardinal Barberini, one of which might be No. 6337: '*il ritratto di S.ta Anna, che ha la S.ma Vergine che le sta sedendo in grembo, et ella trattiene il bambino Giesù che scherza con S. Gio. Battista, in un paese, ma non finito; essendo solo le figure principali ridotte a buon termine, et di questo ne fa mentione il Vasario nella vita del medesimo Leonardo*' ('the [representation?] of S. Anne, who has the Most Holy Virgin sitting in her lap. She holds the child Jesus, who is playing with S. John the Baptist, in a landscape, but not finished; only the principal figures being well realised. Vasari makes a reference to this work in his life of Leonardo'; letter of 16 November 1639 to Cassiano Dal Pozzo). True, this offer for Cardinal Barberini's '*galleria*' might seem to refer to a picture rather than a drawing; the text was apparently so understood by the editor of the letter.[34] However that may be, it appears that the Arconati did own a cartoon (or, if preferred, the first sketch for a cartoon) of S. Anne, assigned to Leonardo. This is stated in a letter to the art-historian Giampietro Bellori (d. 1696) from Resta: '*Lodovico XII, re di Francia, prima del 1500 ordinò un cartone di S. Anna a Lionardo da Vinci, dimorante in Milano al servizio di Lodovico il Moro. Ne fece Leonardo un primo schizzo, che sta presso a' signori conti Arconati in Milano*' ('Louis XII, King of France, ordered a cartoon of S. Anne from Leonardo da Vinci before 1500, when Leonardo was living in Milan in the service of Lodovico il Moro. Leonardo made a first sketch for it, now in the possession of the Counts Arconati in Milan').[35] Presumably identical with this is the drawing recorded by Edward Wright, apparently in 1722. He writes of 'A Holy Family, the same which is painted in oil in the sacristy of S. Celsus . . . as big as the life' among other drawings including the figures appearing in Leonardo's 'Last Supper'; his comparison specifies the design of the picture in the Louvre, which would be an example of a frequent confusion if No. 6337 is referred to. He records that all these drawings had been sold, a year or so before he saw them, by 'Count Alconati' [Conte Giuseppe Arconati] to the 'Marquis Casenedi [Casnedi], the son'.[36] The Casnedi drawings (including at least those of the figures in the 'Last Supper') passed not later than April 1726 into the Sagredo Collection, Venice,[37] where these figures (but not Wright's 'Holy Family') were recorded about 1751 by

Cochin.[38] These figures were sold by the Sagredo family to the British Consul at Venice, John Udny, who stated that they were already in England by Christmas 1763.[39] In this record, again, Wright's 'Holy Family' is not mentioned; but it may well have remained with the other drawings, since it is probably to be identified in a sale at Prestage's, 2–4 February 1764 (Lugt, No. 1346). In one edition of the sale catalogue, lot 52 of the second day was described as the figures of the 'Last Supper' and 'a Drawing for the *Madonna* in the same Church' (S. Maria delle Grazie in Milan is what is claimed, presumably in error), all of which had been bought from the Sagredo; in another edition, this lot is numbered 145, the description being similar except that, as an addition, the Sagredo are stated (wrongly) to have had all the drawings for 'near 100 years'. Perhaps the lot was bought in, since later the figures of the 'Last Supper' are recorded in the possession of Robert Udny, John's brother.[40]

In 1779, identifiable for the first time without a doubt, No. 6337 was in the possession of the Royal Academy,[41] which had been founded in 1768. Its acquisition is not specified in the Royal Academy Minutes, the first mention in these being of a decision to make some repairs to it on 23 March 1791.[42] In 1962, after the National Art-Collections Fund had raised a public subscription to acquire it from the Royal Academy, large contributions being made by the Fund itself, by the Pilgrim Trust and by the National Gallery from its Annual Grant, and after an unprecedented Special Grant had been made from the Exchequer, the cartoon was presented to the National Gallery by the National Art-Collections Fund.

EXHIBITED: 1855, British Institution, No. 140; 1870, Royal Academy, No. 230*; 1896, R.A., No. 166; 1919, Burlington Fine Arts Club (Catalogue, p. 37); April 1924, National Gallery (Centenary of its Foundation); 1930, R.A., No. 630 (*Memorial Catalogue*, No. 680); 1950, R.A., No. 249; 1952, R.A., No. 109; 1953, R.A., No. 41; 1960, R.A., No. 598. The cartoon was for many years on view in the Diploma Gallery at Burlington House.

ENGRAVED: by Anker Smith (impression exhibited at the R.A. 1798, No. 549).

COMPOSITIONAL STUDIES: For these, see the text above.

VERSIONS, COPIES AND DERIVATIONS: A drawing of the heads of the Virgin and S. Anne, closely corresponding, ascribed to Sodoma (1477–1549) is in the Norman Mackenzie Art Gallery, Regina, Canada (cf. W. G. Constable in *Old Master Drawings*, Vol. IX, 1934, p. 28 and Pl. 30). A drawing, apparently after the head of the Virgin, was in the Earl of Pembroke Sale, 10 July 1917 (lot 469); reproduced by S. Arthur Strong, *Drawings by the Old Masters . . . at Wilton House*, Part VI, 1902, No. 63.
    Reference has already been made to a picture in the Ambrosiana, Milan, which follows the cartoon very well, but includes an extra figure, presumably of S. Joseph; it is accepted as being by the Milanese Bernardino Luini (died 1532) and is datable from the costume (note in the Gallery archives by Stella Mary Pearce) probably *ca.* 1530. See Ottino, *Luini*, 1956, No. 132 and Fig. 113; size, 1·15 × 0·91. Cardinal Federico Borromeo's interesting catalogue entry for this picture is sometimes read as claiming collaboration between Leonardo and Luini; but it seems clear that he merely knew of a cartoon by Leonardo, presumably No. 6337, and considered that Luini followed its design in painting this picture (*Federici Cardinalis Borromaei Archiespisc Mediolani Musaeum*, 1625, edition by Luigi Grasselli and Luca Beltrami, 1909, p. 21; the marginal heading for the entry is '*Luini Tabula desumpta à Leonardo*'). Another picture fairly closely corresponding with this, from the King of Holland's sale in 1850, is or was at Neuwied (*Gemälde-Sammlung aus dem Besitz der fürstlichen Familie zu Wied*, 1927, reproduced; size, 1·25 × 0·98). A related picture was lent by Professor Léopold Mabilleau to the Leonardo Exhibition at Milan, 1939 (Catalogue, p. 179, size

1·37 × 1·12); reproduced in the large volume, *Leonardo da Vinci, Edizione curata dalla Mostra di Leonardo da Vinci in Milano*, 1939, p. 73). Another, apparently, then belonged to Professor Lauritz Weibull at Lund (presumably reproduced in the same volume, p. 77, lettered as in the Ambrosiana —the reproduction on p. 79, lettered as Prof. Weibull's, does seem to be of the Ambrosiana picture). A drawing at Venice has been tentatively associated, as a copy, with the Virgin's head in the Ambrosiana picture (L. H. Heydenreich, *I Disegni di Leonardo da Vinci e della sua Scuola conservati nella Galleria dell'Accademia di Venezia*, 1949, Pl. XLIII; also reproduced by A. Rosenberg, *Leonardo da Vinci*, 1903, p. 91). A drawing at Dijon is also claimed to be connected with the Ambrosiana picture (Ottino, *Luini*, 1956, p. 144, No. 5).

A picture stated to be in tempera on canvas, assigned to Bernardino Luini, and thought to be painted from the cartoon that had belonged to his son Aurelio Luini, was in the 18th century in the domestic chapel of the Venini, contrada di Chiaravalle, Milan; it had been sold to them by the Mauri, who thought it to be by Leonardo (this mostly from the notes of Venanzio De Pagave; published by Carlo Amoretti, *Memorie Storiche . . . di Lionardo da Vinci*, 1804, pp. 83 and 165; when prefixed to the 1804 edition of Leonardo's *Trattato della Pittura*, the page numbers are 91 and 173).

A derivation was in Genoa in 1920 (see L. Artù Pettorelli in the *Rassegna d'Arte*, 1920, pp. 197 ff.). Another picture, knee-length and varied, was in 1939 in the Soprani Collection in Milan (reproduced in the large volume, *Leonardo da Vinci*, 1939, p. 81). A design on canvas, attributed to Leonardo, was in 1939 in the Schlumberger Collection in Vienna (also reproduced in the large volume, *Leonardo da Vinci*, 1939, p. 80).

Among derivations from the pose of the Virgin in No. 6337, a clear case is in the 'Vertumnus and Pomona', accepted as by Melzi (1493– *ca.* 1570), formerly at Berlin (Suida, *Leonardo und sein Kreis*, 1929, Fig. 299). Another picture, stated to be (or have been) in the Berlin Depôt, shows a fuller derivation from the Virgin and Child (Suida, *op. cit.*, Fig. 335); Suida attributed it to Fernando de Llanos, but Post, *History of Spanish Painting*, Vol. XI, 1953, p. 275, does not accept this, and seems to think the picture Italian. Suida claimed that the pose of the Virgin in No. 6337 is also reflected in 'The Rest on the Flight into Egypt' of 1515 by Andrea Solari (d. 1524) in the Poldi Pezzoli Museum, Milan (Suida, *op. cit.*, p. 130 and Fig. 241).

Mention has been made above of two works that have suggested an influence of the cartoon in Florence: a drawing by Michelangelo now at Oxford (Berenson, *Florentine Drawings*, No. 1561; J. Wilde in *The Burlington Magazine*, March 1953, pp. 65 ff.; K. T. Parker, *Catalogue of the Collection of Drawings in the Ashmolean Museum*, 1956, Vol. II, No. 291, with comments); and Raphael's altarpiece, the 'Madonna di Foligno' of *ca.* 1511–12 in the Vatican Gallery. The Virgin and Child in Cesare da Sesto's altarpiece in the Castello Sforzesco at Milan (Suida, *op. cit.*, p. 130 and Fig. 294) is presumably derived from the Raphael.

It may be that parts of No. 6337 are freely imitated in other works, but it is difficult to exclude that different inventions by Leonardo are the sources. It has been claimed, for instance, that the Child is imitated in the '*Pala Sforzesca*' (*ca.* 1495) in the Brera Gallery (E. Hildebrandt, *Leonardo da Vinci*, 1927, pp. 130–1 and Fig. 11); this, if it were established, would be important for the date of the cartoon, but the connection appears doubtful, at best.

GENERAL REFERENCE: The basic work is by A. Marks, *The St. Anne of Leonardo da Vinci*, read on 28 June 1882 at the Royal Society of Literature, and reprinted from the Society's *Transactions*.

NOTES: (**1**) There are eight sheets of paper, which appear to be attached directly to the very fine canvas. This is fixed to the rather frail stretcher along the bottom by iron nails at the front; these show strongly through the paper. Irregular amounts of the paper are turned over the stretcher on all sides, except that at the bottom, left centre, it does not now reach to the foot of the stretcher. In places, the paper turned over the stretcher appears to have been reduced at the edges, but it is very unlikely that any significant part of the cartoon has been lost. (**2**) It should be recorded that a picture accepted as the work of the Milanese painter Bernardino Luini in the Ambrosiana at Milan follows the outlines of the figures well; a full-size photograph of Christ's head and hand in the cartoon was compared with the picture, and the scale seemed exactly the same (for this picture see further under VERSIONS). (**3**) There is no doubt of S. Anne's identity; yet it has been and still is often believed that the figure on whose lap the Virgin sits is S. Elizabeth, mother of S. John. The picture by Luini in the Ambrosiana, just mentioned (note 2) as corresponding closely with No. 6337, is curious in this respect; in the act of donation by Cardinal Federico Borromeo in 1618

S. Anne is correctly identified (G. Galbiati, *Itinerario dell'Ambrosiana*, 1951, p. 267), but the Cardinal in his book *Musaeum*, 1625, calls the figure S. Elizabeth (ed. by Luigi Grasselli and Luca Beltrami, 1909, p. 22). (**4**) Reproduced by Jean Alazard, *Orsanmichele* (Memoranda series, undated), p. 61; cf. Fabriczy in the Prussian *Jahrbuch*, 1909, *Beiheft*, p. 32. A Tuscan picture with this motif, often cited in connection, is at Pisa, assigned to Benozzo (Gozzoli). (**5**) Leonardo '*ha facto solo dopoi che è ad Firenci uno schizo in un cartone: finge uno Christo bambino de età circa uno anno che uscendo quasi de bracci ad la mamma, piglia uno agnello et pare che lo stringa. La mamma quasi levandose de grembo ad S.ta Anna, piglia el bambino per spiccarlo da lo agnellino (animale immolatile) che significa Passione. Santa Anna alquanto levandose da sedere, pare che voglia ritenere la figliola che non spicca el bambino da lo agnellino, che forsi vole figurare la Chiesa che non vorrebbe fussi impedita la passione di Christo. Et sono queste figure grande al naturale, ma stano in piccolo cartone, perchè tutte o sedeno o stano curve et una stae alquanto dinanzi ad l'altra verso la man sinistra: et questo schizo ancora non è finito.*' The significance of the lamb seems to have caused Fra Pietro no difficulty; yet it may be that the motif of the Infant Christ in action with a lamb made its first appearance in Italian Renaissance Art in this cartoon of 1500–01 and the drawings leading up to it. (But see further in note 8, two prints assigned to the Master of the Sforza Book of Hours.) (**6**) This seems implied by another letter from Fra Pietro, for the purpose of writing which he says he went to see Leonardo. The date of this second letter is given as 4 April 1501, and references to Easter, which was on 11 April in 1501, show that this can hardly be correct, as has been pointed out by several writers (perhaps first by A. Marks in *The Magazine of Art*, 1893, p. 187); this letter was published by G. L. Calvi from the Milanese archives in 1869, and it is not clear that anyone has seen it since, but the original MS. deserves to be studied. (**7**) The two editions of Vasari (1550 and 1568) correspond except for one change, apparently insignificant ('*In questo mezo*' to '*Finalmente*' at the beginning). Vasari is often supposed to have stated that this cartoon was for the high-altarpiece of the Servite Church of the SS. Annunziata in Florence. This is not the case, as Poggi noticed (*Leonardo da Vinci, La Vita di Giorgio Vasari, nuovamente commentata*, 1919, pp. XVII–XVIII); indeed, Vasari's text taken literally denies it (for the Servites '*nè mai cominciò nulla*', he never began anything). Yet, even if Vasari was meaning to connect this cartoon with work for the high altar of the Annunziata, there are good reasons for disbelief; see particularly Nello Tarchiani in the large volume *Leonardo da Vinci, Edizione curata dalla Mostra di Leonardo da Vinci*, Milan, 1939, p. 100. It is true, as Michael Levey pointed out, that one of the Chapels of the Annunziata contains an altar-piece of 1543 by Antonio di Donnino, showing the Virgin and Child, S. Anne and other Saints; see Milanesi's edition of Vasari, Vol. V, pp. 199–200 and the reproduction in *L'Arte*, January–June 1957, p. 14. (**8**) A. Marks, *The St. Anne of Leonardo da Vinci* (*Transactions of the Royal Society of Literature*, London), 1882, pp. 23 ff. of the offprint, and E. MacCurdy, *Leonardo da Vinci*, 1904, pp. 119–20 and 1933, pp. 195–96, make critical comments on Vasari's text. As Marks points out, the frontispiece of Rigollot's *Catalogue de l'œuvre de Léonard de Vinci*, 1849, is a print of No. 6337, with a lamb added. Although Leonardo could have made a composition with both S. John and a lamb, it should be noted that the lamb would probably not have been included as S. John's emblem. A Lamb is indeed a frequent emblem of S. John in Northern art (van Eyck, etc.) and does so appear in Italian 15th-century painting (*e.g.*, in the polyptych of 1475 by Bartolomeo Vivarini and Studio in the Accademia at Venice, No. 183 of the Catalogue *Opere d'Arte dei Secoli XIV e XV*, 1955, reproduced); but it seems to be rare in Italy at this time. As for works associated with Milan, the Infant Christ, S. John and a lamb are shown in two prints assigned to the Master of the Sforza Book of Hours (Hind, *Early Italian Engraving*, Vol. VI, 1948, Pl. 602 and 603); whether or not the treatment has any relevance here, there is some reason (on grounds of costume) to prefer for these prints a date soon after 1500 to one before. Kaftal in his *Iconography of the Saints in Tuscan Painting* (up to *ca.* 1500), 1952, does not cite a Lamb as an emblem of S. John, except indeed for Its appearance in a scene; even later, this emblem appears to be still unusual in Florence. This matter is touched on by Emile Mâle, *Les Saints Compagnons du Christ*, 1958, pp. 46 ff., esp. p. 51. (**9**) See Vasari; also Billi and the Anonimo Gaddiano (Beltrami, *Documenti e Memorie riguardanti la Vita e le Opere di Leonardo da Vinci*, 1919, No. 254). Resta (see later on in the text and note 35) brings in Louis XII à propos of Leonardo's cartoons of this subject; his statement seems very likely to be unreliable as it stands, and it is beyond the scope of this entry to try to extract from it any worth-while hypothesis concerning their origin. (**10**) Beltrami, *op. cit.*, No. 238. It is uncertain if Giovio's record of a picture of the subject in France (Beltrami, *op. cit.*, No. 258) is based on reliable inform-ation. (**11**) See entry for this picture in the catalogue *Hommage à Léonard de Vinci*, Paris, 1952, pp. 35 ff. The date is uncertain, and it cannot be excluded that the execution dragged over several years. (**12**) In the British Museum Catalogue by A. E. Popham and Philip Pouncey, *Italian Drawings, XIV and XV centuries*, 1950, however, the National Gallery cartoon is dated probably 1500–05; objections to this view are stated by Cecil Gould in the Catalogue of the Leonardo Exhibition at the Royal Academy, 1952 (No. 109). C. Pedretti, *Documenti e Memorie riguardanti Leonardo da Vinci a Bologna e in Emilia*, 1953, pp. 72 ff., even dates it 1508–10. (**13**) The picture shows the Virgin seated on S. Anne's lap, and bending down to hold the Infant Christ, Who is placing Himself astride a lamb. This corresponds quite well with Fra Pietro's description of the Florentine cartoon, except for the action of S. Anne; but some critics have attempted to separate the two compositions. According to one view (see John Shapley in *The Art Bulletin*, Vol. VII, March 1925, pp. 96 ff., and Carlo Pedretti, *Leonardo da Vinci e il poeta bolognese Gerolamo Pandolfi da Casio de' Medici*, 1951, p. 6, and *Documenti e Memorie riguardanti Leonardo da Vinci a Bologna e in Emilia*, 1953, pp. 65 ff. and 79 ff.), the Florentine cartoon corresponded for the most part with a drawing now at Venice. This drawing is recorded as autograph by Popham (*The Drawings of Leonardo da Vinci*, 1947, No. 174A); and, although it is not always thought to be by Leonardo's hand, there seems at least no need to doubt that it records an idea of Leonardo's for the subject. It shows links with No. 6337, but includes a lamb instead of S. John the Baptist; and it does correspond well with Fra Pietro's description of the Florentine cartoon. A different view, propounded by W. Suida, *Leonardo und sein Kreis*, 1929, p. 131 and Fig. 131 (right-hand side of the page), is that the cartoon of 1500/1 is reflected in a picture assigned to Brescianino formerly at Berlin, and in a similar picture, No. 505, in the Prado Museum. Sir Kenneth Clark, *Leonardo da Vinci*, 1939, p. 110, thinks that the composition of Raphael's 'Madonna with a Lamb' in the Prado, apparently of 1507, which may indeed have been influenced by Leonardo's cartoon of 1500/1, is closely related to the pictures assigned to Brescianino, but has no resemblance to No. 6337 or to Leonardo's picture in the Louvre. Further, in the *Catalogue of the Drawings of Leonardo da Vinci at Windsor Castle*, 1935, he suggests that a drawing at Windsor, No. 12534, is connected with the Brescianino design; but Popham, *The Drawings of Leonardo da Vinci*, 1947, pp. 74–75, is reserved about this. (**14**) Cf. the 'Madonna with the Yarn-winder'; Klassiker der Kunst *Leonardo*, 1931, Pl. 65–7, and R. Langton Douglas, *Leonardo da Vinci*, 1944, p. 29 in conjunction with his *A few Italian Pictures collected by Godfrey Locker-Lampson*, Pl. XII. (**15**) C. Pedretti, *Documenti e Memorie riguardanti Leonardo da Vinci a Bologna e in Emilia*, 1953, pp. 83 ff. (**16**) Casio wrote an epitaph on Fra Pietro (Pedretti, *op. cit.*, p. 87), and perhaps was acquainted with him. (**17**) It does not appear that there is any trace of a restraining right hand of S. Anne in the Louvre picture; but a right hand that may be considered restraining is seen in a version of the composition in the Brera (Klassiker der Kunst *Leonardo*, 1931, Pl. 62). If the Louvre picture were shown to have or have had a similar hand, the argument in the text would need to be modified; yet it would still remain an argument for dating No. 6337 earlier than the missing Florentine cartoon and the Louvre picture. (**18**) Notes in the Gallery archives by Stella Mary Pearce. (**19**) A. E. Popham, *The Drawings of Leonardo da Vinci*, 1947, p. 74 and Nos. 175, 174B and 174A. The claim that the drawing at Venice records the composition of Leonardo's missing Florentine cartoon has been recorded in note 13. (**20**) E.g. by L. H. Heydenreich in the *Gazette des Beaux-Arts*, 1933, II, pp. 205 ff., by Popham in his book on Leonardo drawings and in Popham and Pouncey's British Museum Catalogue (both already referred to). (**21**) Popham, *op. cit.*, No. 181, further records a drawing of infants at Windsor, as connected at least in character with the National Gallery cartoon. A drawing in the Louvre, perhaps for the head of S. John in the 'Virgin of the Rocks', has sometimes been associated with the head of Christ in the cartoon; but this is unconvincing (Berenson, No. 1067 and Fig. 487; see the entry for the 'Virgin of the Rocks' in the National Gallery Catalogue, *The Earlier Italian Schools*, 1961, under Drawings, and note 42 there). (**22**) *Federici Cardinalis Borromaei Archiepisc Mediolani Musaeum*, 1625; edition by Luigi Grasselli and Luca Beltrami, 1909, p. 22. (**23**) Lomazzo, *Trattato*, 1584, p. 127; cf. Achille Ratti (Pope Pius XI) in the *Rassegna d'Arte*, 1912, p. 34. (**24**) Sir Kenneth Clark, *Leonardo da Vinci*, 1939, p. 147 (Windsor, Nos. 12519 and 12567). (**25**) A. E. Popham, *The Drawings of Leonardo da Vinci*, 1947, p. 73. (**26**) Bernard Berenson, *The Drawings of the Florentine Painters*, 1938, Vol. I, p. 175. (**27**) Suida, *Leonardo und sein Kreis*, 1929, p. 130. (**28**) See the Illustrated Catalogue, pp. xvi and lxix (Unillustrated Catalogue, pp. xiv and lxx). (**29**) Luca Beltrami, *Luini*, 1911, p. 556. When Cavenaghi was cleaning Luini's picture, he also considered this possibility; the matter is discussed by Achille Ratti (Pope Pius XI) in the *Rassegna d'Arte*, 1912, p. 37. (**30**) See the criticism of this in the *Raccolta Vinciana*, Vol. X, 1919, pp. 271 ff., and the elaborate essay by Meyer Schapiro in the *Journal of the History of Ideas*, Vol. XVII, 1956, pp. 147 ff. (**31**) *E.g.*, in part of a television talk, printed in a pamphlet on the cartoon produced by the National Art-Collections Fund in aid of the Appeal to acquire it for the nation, 1962. (**32**) Lomazzo, *Trattato*, 1584, p. 171. Lomazzo says, apparently, that many copies had been drawn from Aurelio Luini's cartoon; possibly the two drawings recorded under Versions, at the beginning, are examples of these. The identification of the picture once in the Venini collection (see under Versions) might (though not probably) be of use for settling the status of Aurelio Luini's cartoon. (**33**) See further under Versions. (**34**) Enrico Carusi, *Lettere di Galeazzo Arconato e Cassiano Dal Pozzo per lavori sui manoscritti di Leonardo da Vinci* in *Accademie e Biblioteche d'Italia*, Anno III, 1929/30, pp. 508 and 513. (**35**) Bottari and Ticozzi, *Raccolta di Lettere*, 1822, Vol. III, p. 481. For the reference to Louis XII, see the comment in note 9. (**36**) Edward Wright, *Some Observations made in travelling through France, Italy &c. in the years MDCCXX, MDCCXXI, and MDCCXXII*, 2nd ed., 1764, p. 471; the first edition has not been consulted. The corrections to the names are from Pino (see next reference). (**37**) Domenico Pino, *Storia Genuina del Cenacolo*, 1796, pp. 69–70, quoting a letter from Padre Maestro Monti, 5 October 1765. Charles Rogers, *A Collection of Prints in Imitation of Drawings*, 1778, Vol. I, p. 9. For the date at which the Casnedi drawings passed into the Sagredo collection, see a letter from A. M. Zanetti, 6 April 1726, in Bottari and Ticozzi, *Raccolta di Lettere*, 1822, Vol. II, p. 171. (**38**) C.-N. Cochin, *Voyage d'Italie*, 1758, Vol. III, p. 146. A manuscript catalogue of the Sagredo drawings by Algarotti is (or was) at Dresden; see H. Posse in the Prussian *Jahrbuch*, 1931, *Beiheft*, pp. 16 and 43. There exists, further, much Sagredo documentation at Venice: see Mario Brunetti in *Arte Veneta*, 1951, pp. 158 ff.; also the reference by A. Blunt, *The Drawings of G. B. Castiglione and Stefano della Bella . . . at Windsor Castle*, 1954, p. 24. (**39**) Pino, *loc. cit.* The date of Udny's purchase of these Sagredo drawings is presumably 1762: see Brunetti, *loc. cit.*, p. 160. (**40**) Charles Rogers, *op. cit.*, 1778, Vol. I, p. 9. Cf. also James Barry, *A Letter to the Dilettanti Society* (1798) in *Works*, 1809, Vol. II, p. 554. In references given in the text to these figures it is assumed that the group remained complete from the time of Wright onwards. (**41**) This is from its being shown in a drawing dated 1779 by E. F. Burney, now owned by the Royal Academy; see J. Byam Shaw in *The Burlington Magazine*, May 1962, p. 212. (**42**) See Marks, pp. 34–35 of the offprint, or Whitley, *Artists and their Friends in England, 1700–1799*, 1928, Vol. I, p. 351.

Eustache LE SUEUR
1616–1655

French School. Baptised at Paris, 16 November 1616. Pupil of Vouet (*q.v.*). In spite of his particular devotion to Raphael and the evident influence of Poussin (*q.v.*), he appears never to have visited Italy. He was a founder member of the Académie Royale established in 1648. He painted a number of altarpieces for Parisian churches, and the majority of his best pictures have a grave and yet intimate religious character. His is a very personal classicism, despite the tendency to 'quote' almost too patently from Raphael—notably from the tapestry designs (*i.e.*, the Cartoons lent from the Royal Collection to the Victoria and Albert Museum). He died in Paris, 30 April 1655.

6299 S. PAUL PREACHING AT EPHESUS

Oil on canvas, 40½ × 34 (1·020 × 0·865). Apparently in good condition, though there are some retouchings over losses here and there.

The subject is S. Paul exhorting the people at Ephesus, where 'many of them also which used curious arts brought their books together, and burned them . . .' (*Acts*, XIX, vv. 18–20).

The picture is likely to be a preliminary sketch or *modello* by Le Sueur in preparation for his large-scale picture of the same subject in Notre Dame, Paris.[1] The Goldsmiths' Guild used to present a painting to Notre Dame annually on 1 May, and since 1630 the subject had been taken from the *Acts of the Apostles*.[2] The large picture for which No. 6299 may well be the preliminary sketch was presented by the Guild as the 'May' of 1649. The instigators of Le Sueur's painting were the goldsmiths Philippe Renaud and Gilles Crévon, and for each of these the artist executed small repetitions,[3] presumably of the large picture. At least one of these seems to survive.[4] Between No. 6299 and the large picture there are a number of differences; and it is recorded by Félibien that there were differences between the *première pensée* of Le Sueur and his final composition.

The picture mentioned and much praised in 1688 by Félibien,[5] which may well be No. 6299 and seems certainly to be the same composition, was in Paris in the collection of Le Normand, *Greffier en chef du Grand Conseil* and secretary to the King. A picture by Le Sueur: 'The burning of the magical books at Ephesus', was in the sale of Dr. Newton, Bishop of Bristol, in London, 30 April 1790, lot 96, and the same picture was in the sale of John Willett, London, 31 May 1813, lot 19. This could have been No. 6299; but the picture in the Girou de Buzareingues collection by 1852[6] and in the Girou de Buzareingues sale, Paris in 1892 (lot 46), is not likely to have been the same. No. 6299 belonged to H. D. Molesworth in 1957. It was bought from Messrs. Colnaghi in 1959 out of Grant-in-Aid.

EXHIBITED : 1957, Manchester, *Art Treasures Centenary* Exhibition, No. 184.

ENGRAVED : by Benoît Audran (d. 1721) in a rectangular format (presumably the Le Normand collection picture and therefore perhaps No. 6299).

DRAWINGS : A drawing of the subject at Frankfort is claimed to be transitional between the present composition and the large picture.[7] A number of drawings related to the subject are in the Louvre.[8]

VERSIONS : for the large picture in Notre Dame de Paris, and two pictures probably painted after it, see above and note 4 below. A version of No. 6299 in the museum at Algiers is published in *Etudes d'Art*, 1947–48, pp. 135–36. Attention has not previously been drawn to its relationship with No. 6299; but it has not been examined in the original for the present entry.

NOTES : (**1**) That picture is reproduced by G. Rouchès, *Eustache Le Sueur*, 1923, Pl. IX. It is discussed, *op. cit.*, pp. 97–100. (**2**) Cf. the article on the subject by J. Guiffrey in *Mémoires Soc. Hist. de Paris*, 1886, Vol. 13, p. 289 ff. (**3**) The fact is recorded by Florent Le Comte *Cabinet . . .* 1702 ed., Vol. III, p. 75. (**4**) In the museum at Schwerin; cf. 1882 catalogue, pp. 613–14. (**5**) *Entretiens sur les vies et sur les ouvrages des plus excellens peintres*, etc., 1688, Vol. V, p. 37 ff. (**6**) Mentioned as there in the article by L. Dussieux in *Archives de l'Art français*, 1852–53, pp. 29–30, note 4. (**7**) Mentioned in the 1957 Manchester catalogue as reproduced in *Stift und Feder*, 1927, No. 31. (**8**) Cf. J. Guiffrey–P Marcel, *Inventaire Général des dessins du Musée du Louvre . . . (Ecole française)*, 1921, Vol. IX, Nos. 9197–9203.

Quinten MASSYS
1465/6–1530

Also spelt Matsys and Metsys. Early Netherlandish School; worked at Antwerp.

6282   THE VIRGIN AND CHILD ENTHRONED, WITH FOUR ANGELS

Oil on oak, painted surface, 24½ × 17 (0·62 × 0·43); rounded top. The flying Angel on the left is largely modern except for the head and arm. The remainder of the picture seems in good condition.

An early work,[1] comparable in style with the more considerable 'Virgin and Child Enthroned' in Brussels, in which also the throne is Gothic and the Child seated behind the book. In such pictures Massys depended a good deal on van Eyck, adapting an already archaic form to the taste of the end of the 15th century. Soon after, he was to effect a major change in his style, partly under the influence of Leonardo (q.v.) and his Milanese followers.

The only other picture in the National Gallery certainly by Massys, 'The Virgin and Child with SS. Barbara (?) and Catherine', is larger, more typical in design and probably a late work; but it is in a different technique and very much damaged.[2]

No. 6282 was in the sale of the Sneyd Heirlooms from Keele Hall, 27 June 1924 (lot 69), bought by Buttery. It passed, by 1927 at latest, to C. W. Dyson Perrins. It was bequeathed by C. W. Dyson Perrins in 1958, together with Turner's 'Palestrina – Composition' (No. 6283), which has since been transferred to the Tate Gallery.

EXHIBITED: 1927, R.A. (No. 171), and 1953–54, R.A. (No. 95); 1956, Bruges (No. 31); 1957, Manchester, *Art Treasures Centenary* Exhibition, No. 26.

NOTES: (1) See Friedländer in *Cicerone*, 1927, pp. 6–7 and his *Die Altniederländische Malerei*. Vol. VII, pp. 31–33 and No. 25. (2) See Martin Davies, *National Gallery Catalogues, Early Netherlandish School*, 2nd edition, 1955, No. 3664. 'The Crucifixion' (No. 715) is catalogued as from the Studio of Massys and 'A Grotesque Old Woman' (No. 5769) as after Massys(?).

HANS MEMLINC
Active 1465, died 1494

Early Netherlandish School; from Seligenstadt near Frankfurt on the Main; worked at Bruges.

6275   THE VIRGIN AND CHILD WITH SAINTS, ANGELS AND DONORS ('THE DONNE TRIPTYCH')

Oil on oak. Painted surfaces: central part 27¾ × 27¾ (0·705 × 0·705); wings (all four surfaces—see below) 27¾ × 12 (0·705 × 0·305). Cleaned on acquisition; in very good condition.[1]

The Child blesses Sir John Donne, who kneels on the left under the protection of S. Catherine. On the right, sponsored by S. Barbara, kneels Sir John's wife Elizabeth; a child who is clearly one of their daughters (? Anne—see below) kneels behind her. Both Sir John and Lady Donne wear the Yorkist collar of roses and suns, with King Edward IV's pendant, the Lion of March.

The splendid portico under which the Virgin is enthroned extends into both wings. On the left is S. John the Baptist, and behind him, outside, a figure often claimed, from the manner in which he appears in the picture, to be the portrait of the painter (see below). On the right is S. John the Evangelist.

As is customary with elaborate early Netherlandish triptychs, the wings, which fold over the centre panel to cover it, have on the reverse paintings in grisaille simulating sculptures: on the left wing S. Christopher carrying the Child; on the right S. Anthony Abbot.

The donors are identified beyond doubt by the coats of arms appearing on two of the capitals shown in the centre panel, and in the window-glass of the right wing.[2] Sir John Donne married Elizabeth, a sister of William, Lord Hastings,[3] not earlier than 1462, probably in 1465 and not later. He was knighted by Edward IV in 1471 at Tewkesbury, after the final defeat of the Lancastrian supporters of Henry VI under Queen Margaret. He died in 1503;[4] his widow in 1507/8.

J. G. Nichols,[5] who identified the donors in 1840, accepted an incorrect record that Sir John Donne was slain at the battle of Edgecote in 1469; and this has also been accepted until recently by writers on the picture. So early a date for it need no longer stand. Since the attribution to Memlinc is now generally accepted,[6] it is probable that the picture was painted in Bruges, where Memlinc lived and worked. Sir John Donne was almost certainly in Bruges for the marriage of Margaret of York to Charles the Bold in 1468,[7] and again in Flanders on a mission in 1477.[8] The picture seems characteristic of Memlinc's developed style; and for this reason alone, if not from the probable age of the daughter depicted (see below), the later of these two dates is to be preferred, if the choice for the commission is thought to be confined to one of the two known visits by Donne to Flanders. He is, however, recorded at several dates in Calais, where he seems to have lived a good deal; and journeys to and from Bruges and Calais could have taken place. In any case the picture need not have been painted immediately upon its commission.

Nothing in such historical evidence as is available is incompatible with a date of about 1480. As to the child, Sir John Donne is known to have had two sons and two daughters. Since one daughter is shown, it would seem that she alone had been born at the time of the painting. There is some reason to believe that this eldest child is Anne, who is unlikely to have been born much earlier than 1470 and may even have been born a few years later. She probably predeceased her mother, since she is not, like the other three children, mentioned in Lady Donne's will.[9]

As has been mentioned above, it has often been supposed that the figure appearing modestly in the left wing is the painter himself. Figures have been considered self-portraits in several of Memlinc's works. Special mention should be made of one in the centre panel of 'The Marriage of S. Catherine' in S. John's Hospital at Bruges,[10] since there is some similarity in the faces there and here. Weale,[11] it is true, states that this figure represents a Brother of the Hospital, which seems reasonable; whereas the costume of the figure in No. 6275 seems purely secular. The man in 'The Marriage of S. Catherine' appears younger and that picture bears the date 1479; but it would be rash to make any deduction from that for the date of No. 6275.

The particular value of the 'Donne Triptych' to the National Collection is that there are few portraits of Englishmen from the 15th century and that very few pictures can have been commissioned by an Englishman of one of the great masters of the early Renaissance. This is moreover the first example to be acquired by the National Gallery of a complete triptych by one of the chief painters of the Early Netherlandish School. Mcmlinc, or his patrons, was particularly fond of this form, and the picture thus displays the character of his art to the full, with its feeling of piety expressed in figures of quiet dignity, harmoniously arranged in a luminous atmosphere and painted with perfect craftsmanship.

Records of the picture earlier than the 18th century have not been found, but a direct genealogical line may be recorded, down which it could have passed. Sir Griffith Donne was a son (though clearly not the eldest son) of Sir John.[12] His sole daughter and heiress Elizabeth (died 1590) married Thomas Hughes.[13] Their daughter Grisold (died 1613) married secondly Francis Clifford, 4th Earl of Cumberland.[14] He died in 1641 and was succeeded by his son Henry, on whose death in 1643 the Earldom of Cumberland became extinct.[15] The heiress to the Clifford fortune was the 5th Earl's daughter Elizabeth (died 1691),[16] who in 1664 married Richard Boyle, created Earl of Burlington. He died in 1698. No. 6275 (with the donors supposed to be Lord Clifford and his Lady) is recorded in the 3rd Earl of Burlington's villa at Chiswick about 1744.[17] The 3rd Earl died in 1753. His daughter Charlotte Elizabeth had married William, Marquess of Hartington. She died in 1754, and in 1755 he succeeded as 4th Duke of Devonshire. The picture is often recorded in the collection of the Dukes of Devonshire at the Chiswick villa[18] (recently restored by the Ministry of Works and open to the public). In December 1892 it was moved to Chatsworth,[19] Derbyshire. It was acquired in 1957 from the Duke of Devonshire's collection in part payment of estate duty, under the terms of the Finance Act, 1956.

EXHIBITED: 1866, South Kensington Museum, *National Portraits* (revised catalogue, No. 18); 1876, Royal Academy (No. 172); 1884, Brighton (No. 141); 1892, Burlington Fine Arts Club (No. 20); 1902, Bruges (No.56); 1906, Guildhall (No. 21); 1909, B.F.A.C. (No. 22); 1927, R.A. (No. 47); 1948, Agnew (No. 33); 1948–52, National Gallery; 1953–54, R.A. (No. 27).

NOTES: (**1**) The two vertical members forming the centre panel had parted at some time and had been joined out of alignment; they had to be separated again and rejoined correctly. On the front of the paintings was much loose paint, but few losses; the most important on the Virgin's face, right centre. Of the reverse paintings 'S. Christopher' is rather more damaged; but even here the condition might be called good. The frame is an imitation of 1957 adapted from an original on a triptych by Memlinc in Bruges. (**2**) The main coat (although rather roughly represented) is safely interpreted as *azure a wolf salient argent*, in one case at least *langued gules*, for Donne. The lady's arms, impaled with Donne on one capital, are *argent a maunch sable*, for Hastings. T. W. Newton Dunn, *The Genealogies of the Dwnns of South Wales*, 1953, No. 39, records from the Visitations (late 16th and early 17th centuries) of Lewis Dwnn 'a field azure and a silver wolf armed red as to the teeth and tongue' as the arms of Sir John Donne's father. Donne, and some other names to be mentioned, are recorded with variations of spelling. (**3**) For the relationship, see N. H. Nicolas, *Testamenta Vetusta*, Vol. I, 1826, p. 372. The Lord Hastings in question is recorded in Burke's *Peerage*, 1956, under

Huntingdon. Mr. K. B. McFarlane has most generously made available his extensive researches on the genealogies and on the picture. (**4**) There existed a different Sir John Donne at this period; cf. Ormerod, *History of Cheshire*, 1882, Vol. II, p. 248. For information about the Sir John Donne of the triptych, see T. W. Newton Dunn, *op. cit.*, No. 45. He is often mentioned in documents of the time. His will and the wills of his wife and of his two sons Edward and Griffith are at Somerset House; photostats in the National Gallery. (**5**) *The Gentleman's Magazine*, 1840, Vol. II, pp. 489 ff. The identification was made independently by Weale in *Notes and Queries*, 3 December 1864, pp. 451–52. (**6**) It seems first to have been made, though tentatively, by Waagen, *Kunstwerke*, 1837, Vol. I, pp. 264–65. The picture is usually treated of at some length in books on Memlinc. (**7**) *Mémoires d'Olivier de La Marche*, ed. H. Beaune and J. d'Arbaumont, Vol. III, 1885, p. 111. The editors give the name as 'Jehan Don' and do not appear to doubt the reading; but they record that in Buchon's edition 'Jehanston' is given. (**8**) Rymer, *Foedera*, Vol. XII, 1711, pp. 42–43; Cora L. Scofield, *The Life and Reign of Edward IV*, 1923, Vol. II, p. 186, records this. The mission was to Ghent (cf. Scofield, p. 185), which is near Bruges; indeed, Bruges may fairly be considered to be on the way to Ghent from England. (**9**) K. B. McFarlane has weighed a mass of evidence to establish probabilities for the dates of birth of the children; he considers that Anne's brothers, Edward and Griffith, and her sister Margaret were probably a good deal younger than she was. (**10**) Reproduced as a presumed self-portrait in the catalogue *Flanders in the Fifteenth Century*, Detroit, October/December 1960, p. 140. (**11**) Weale, *Hans Memlinc*, 1901, p. 37. (**12**) He died in 1543/4; his brother Sir Edward Donne died in 1552. (**13**) Monumental inscription in North Mimms Church, given by Robert Clutterbuck, *History . . . of Hertfordshire*, Vol. I, 1815, p. 463. (**14**) Monumental inscription in Londesborough Church, given by T. D. Whitaker, *The History and Antiquities of the Deanery of Craven*, 3rd edition, 1878, p. 359. Cf. also the record on the Clifford family picture (Whitaker, pp. 346–47). Another way in which the picture could have passed to the Cliffords is mentioned in note 15; it seems less likely. (**15**) An engraving of the heads of Sir John and Lady Donne was published in 1793 by J. Thane, 'From an ancient Picture on Board in the Possession of John Thane'. The heads are described as representing George Talbot, 4th Earl of Shrewsbury, and Anne his first wife, with a date 1478. Cf. G. Scharf in *Archaeologia*, Vol. XL, 1866, p. 473. This Lady Shrewsbury was indeed a Hastings, being a daughter of William, Lord Hastings, and thus a niece of Lady Donne. The arms seen on the capitals and in the glass of No. 6275 are added (more or less accurately) on the print. Perhaps the Donne arms were supposed to show a talbot (dog); talbots are certainly associated with the Shrewsburys as supporters of their arms and as their badge, but never apparently formed their coat of arms. The animal shown in No. 6275 is not in any case reasonably identified as a talbot. Nevertheless, it should be recorded that Margaret, one of the daughters, and perhaps the eldest daughter, of this Earl and Countess of Shrewsbury, was the first wife of Henry, 1st Earl of Cumberland, and this would link up with the history of No. 6275 suggested above. The 4th Earl of Shrewsbury was overseer of Lady Donne's will, and was sufficiently interested in her welfare in 1503 to write on her behalf to Sir Reginald Bray. Thus the descent of the picture via Lady Donne's niece cannot at present be excluded. But (apart from the heraldic objections) this identification of the sitters is impossible from the dates. The 4th Earl of Shrewsbury was born in 1468; at Memlinc's death in 1494 he was twenty-six. Further, he was made a Knight of the Garter in 1488, and one might well be puzzled if thereafter he were depicted without any indication of it. But it is not credible that the donor in No. 6275 is under twenty, or even under twenty-six. The print is from a (partial?) version or copy of No. 6275, presumably the picture without attribution, lot 65 of the Thane sale, 2 March 1820, 'George Talbot, Earl of Shrewsbury, and his first Couness, 1618' [*sic*]—the date on the print could carelessly be read as 1418. John Thane (d. 1818) is recorded in the *D.N.B.* and elsewhere. (**16**) Her will is at Somerset House. (**17**) *Vertue*, published by The Walpole Society, Vol. V, pp. 30–31. The attribution was to Jan van Eyck, 'his name burnt in on the back'. No. 6275 has indeed on the back *IOHANES VAN EYCK*, apparently in black pigment (Scharf in *Archaeologia*, Vol. XL, 1866, p. 472, says black ink). (**18**) *E.g.*, *London and its Environs Described*, Vol. II, 1761, p. 122. Here a date 1444 is added to the attribution to Jan van Eyck. The back of No. 6275 is now partly obscured by wax, but no date seems to be written there (Scharf, *loc. cit.*, in previous note, records none); to the right of the name, nevertheless, the panel has been buttoned for conservation, and a date might formerly have been legible in that place. Among later records of the picture at Chiswick, see Walpole, *Anecdotes*, Vol. I, 1762, p. 26 (Dallaway's edition, Vol. I, 1826, pp. 50–51); J. J. Volkmann, *Neueste Reisen durch England*, Vol. II,

1782, p. 440; Neale's *Views of Seats*, 2nd Series, Vol. V, 1829: see also Louis Simond, *Voyage en Angleterre*, 2nd edition consulted, 1817, Vol. II, p. 161 (April 1811), or English translation, 1815, Vol. II, p. 119, who is less explicit, but is surely recording the same. (**19**) Illustrated Catalogue of the B.F.A.C. Exhibition, *Early Netherlandish Pictures*, 1892, p. xv. The home of the Memlinc in the Devonshire collection until then appears constantly to have been Chiswick, although indeed the pictures there were off the walls for a time for James Wyatt's additions of 1788 (now removed) to the house (see Lysons, *Environs of London*, Vol. II, 1795, p. 195; passage modified in the second edition, Vol. II, Part I, 1811, p. 125). Some confusion was caused by Passavant, *Kunstreise*, 1833, p. 72, who identified the picture mentioned by Walpole (see previous note), not with No. 6275 but wrongly with another picture in the Devonshire collection, now associated with Pieter Pourbus. This picture, seen at Devonshire House, London, by Passavant, appears to have been in that house already by 1743 (*Vertue*, published by The Walpole Society, Vol. V, p. 23, 'a Quire. of priest & religion'); it is reproduced by S. Arthur Strong, *The Masterpieces in The Duke of Devonshire's Collection of Pictures*, 1901, Pl. 17.

Jean-François MILLET
1814–1875

French School; worked in Paris, at Barbizon and in Normandy.

Ascribed to J.-F. MILLET

6253   LANDSCAPE WITH BUILDINGS

Oil on canvas, $14\frac{1}{2} \times 17\frac{1}{2}$ (0·369 × 0·445).
Inscribed: *F. Millet*, followed by an illegible date.
Bequeathed by Sir Victor Wellesley, 1954.

Claude-Oscar MONET
1840–1926

French School; worked in Paris and the region, also in London and Venice.

6278 L'INONDATION

Oil on canvas, 28 × 36 (0·71 × 0·915). Apparently in excellent condition.
Stamped: *Claude Monet*.[1]

A similar picture is signed by Monet and dated 1896.[2] The subject of both is said to be the flood waters of the river Epte. This is a tributary of the Seine which passes through Giverny, the village, roughly mid-way between Paris and Rouen, where Monet lived for more than forty years, and where he died. At this time, in the 1890's, much of Monet's output consisted of series of pictures of the same subject under different lighting conditions—hay-stacks, poplars or the façade of Rouen Cathedral. But, though Monet had painted a number of snow and ice scenes, the present picture is not part of a series of this kind. The only other version, already mentioned, differs from it in including more foreground and more of the upper part of the trees, and above all in showing much more placid water, thereby permitting more precise reflection of the trunks of the trees. This implies some sacrifice of natural appearances to pictorial ends and thus strongly suggests that the National Gallery picture may have been painted on the spot, the other in the studio, later. No. 6278, being unsigned by Monet and therefore considered by him unfinished, would thus constitute the sketch for the other, finished, picture.

No. 6278 was sold by Michel Monet, the artist's son, to a private collector, who sold it to the Galerie Charpentier, Paris. It was bought from the latter by Arthur Tooth & Sons, who exhibited it in London in 1957.[3] It was purchased from Messrs. Tooth, 1958, out of the Clarke, Florence and Temple-West Funds, and the Long-field Memorial, with a contribution from J. McGown.

REFERENCES: (1) This is the stamp which was put on unsigned pictures found in Monet's studio at his death. Douglas Cooper, in a letter to *The Times* newspaper of 17 May 1958, claims that he saw a false signature on the picture 'two months ago'. This is disproved, at least as regards the date, by a photograph of the picture in the Gallery's possession dated Paris, 28 February 1958 which shows no signature. (2) Reproduced, among other places, in Claude Roger-Marx's *Monet*, 1949, Pl. 48. (3) As '*L'Inondation: Bords de l'Epte*' with a suggested dating *ca.* 1884.

BARTOLOMÉ ESTEBAN MURILLO
1617–1682

Spanish School; worked in Seville.

6153 SELF-PORTRAIT

Oil on canvas, $48\frac{1}{4} \times 42$ ($1 \cdot 22 \times 1 \cdot 07$). Apparently in excellent condition.[1]

Signed and inscribed: *Bart.us Murillo seipsum depin/gens pro filiorum votis acpreci/bus explendis* (Bart.us Murillo portraying himself to satisfy the wishes and prayers of his children).

This is probably one of the two self-portraits by Murillo which are mentioned by Palomino, writing some forty-two years after the artist's death.[2] In spite of its official appearance we must take it, in view of the inscription, to be a personal work done for the painter's family. It is not possible to say exactly who are the children referred to in the inscription, because for the most part the dates of their deaths are not recorded and because the date of the picture's execution is uncertain. It has usually been considered a late work,[3] but Waterhouse has recently suggested a date 'perhaps hardly later than 1655'.[4] Of Murillo's nine children whose baptisms are recorded, two were baptised after 1655.[5] Only three of the nine are mentioned in his will: Doña Francisca, baptised 8 February 1655, who is later described as a nun and who, it seems, renounced her inheritance, Don Gabriel, baptised 20 March 1657, who at the time of his father's death was in the 'Indies', and Don Gaspar, baptised 22 October 1661. These two sons were named as the chief heirs.[6] Whether in fact this picture was in the possession

5—A.G.

of Murillo's family after his death is not known. Palomino records a self-portrait by him in the possession of Don Gaspar Murillo, but from the description this was clearly not No. 6153.[7]

In the year of the painter's death, No. 6153 was sent to Brussels to be engraved for Nicholas Omazurinus,[8] who may be mentioned in Murillo's will as Nicolas Olnasur[9] and may have been the Nicolas Omazur, poet and merchant of Antwerp, born 23 September 1609.[10] Perhaps already by the early 18th century it was owned by Sir Daniel Arthur, 'a rich Irish merchant who died in Spain', by 1728/9 it had been made over by his widow to her next husband Mr. Bagnall.[11] Before 1740, as Vertue records, Bagnall had sold it to Frederick, Prince of Wales, the father of George III.[12] It is recorded in the Household Accounts for 1747.[13] In 1750 it is again recorded by Vertue as part of the Prince of Wales' Collection;[14] but Frederick died in 1751, and its history is uncertain until 1794, when it was sold with the collection of Sir Lawrence Dundas.[15] It was probably bought at this sale by Lord Ashburnham, in whose house in Dover Street, London, it appears to have been seen in 1804.[16] It was sold by the Earl of Ashburnham in 1850[17] and was probably bought by the Earl Spencer, for in the following year it is recorded at Althorp House.[18] It was bought from the Earl Spencer in 1953 out of the Grant-in-Aid.

EXHIBITED: 1855, British Institution, No. 53; 1857, Manchester, *Art Treasures*, No. 640; 1868, Leeds, No. 342; 1876–80, South Kensington Museum, No. 77;[19] 1895–96, London, The New Gallery, No. 103; 1913–14, Grafton Galleries, No. 99; 1920, Royal Academy, No. 83; 1947, Agnew's, Exhibiton of *Pictures from Althorp*, No. 22; 1951, Edinburgh, Arts Council, *Spanish Paintings*, No. 28.

ENGRAVINGS:[20] Richard Collin, Brussels, 1682, inscribed *Bartholomeus Morillus Hispalensis/se-ipsum depingens pro filiorum votis ac precibus explendis/Nicolaus Omazurinus Antverpiensis/Tanti viri simula-crum in Amicitiæ Symbolon/in æs incidi Mandauit. Anno 1682* ('Bartholomew Murillo of Spain portraying himself to satisfy the wishes and prayers of his children Nicolas Omazurinus of Antwerp ordered the likeness of so great a man to be engraved as a symbol of friendship. In the year 1682'); R. Collin in J. Sandrart, *Academia nobilissimae Artis pictoriae*, 1683, facing p. 392; Anon., in D'Argenville, *Abregé de la vie des plus fameux peintres*, new ed., 1762, Vol. II, p. 254; Benedetto Eredia; Luigi Calamatta (lithograph).

COPIES: Duke of Wellington Collection (Curtis, No. 464); Prado Museum, No. 1153 as by Alonso Miguel Tobar, and No. 2912; Petworth, No. 68.

NOTES: (1) It was cleaned not long before acquisition, probably in 1951. (2) A. Palomino, *El Museo Pictorico*, etc., 1797, Vol. II, p. 625 (1st ed. 1724): '*Hizo tambien su retrato á instancias de sus hijos, cosa maravillosa, el qual está abierto en estampa en Flandes por Nicolás Amazurino*...'(3) 'The artist is represented as about sixty years of age', C. B. Curtis, *Velazquez and Murillo*, 1883, No. 462, pp. 293–4. A. L. Mayer suggested a date *ca.* 1675, see the frontispiece, *Murillo*, Klassiker der Kunst, 1913. (4) E. K. Waterhouse, Catalogue, *Exhibition of Spanish Paintings*, Arts Council, Edinburgh, 1951, No. 28. (5) See J. Cascales Muñoz, *Las Bellas Artes Plásticas en Sevilla*, 1929, Vol. I, p. 120, where the names and dates of baptism of Murillo's nine children are given. (6) Murillo's will is published in Sir William Stirling Maxwell, *Annals of the Artists in Spain*, 1891, Vol. 3, p. 1059, footnote 4, following. For the dates of baptism see note 5. (7) Palomino, *loc. cit.* (8) See under Engravings. (9) See Sir William Stirling Maxwell, *loc. cit.* (10) See the *Biographie Nationale*, 1901, Vol. 16, p. 167. (11) *Diary of the First Earl of Egmont*, Historical Manuscripts Commission, 1923, Vol. 3, p. 344—entry for 3 February 1728/9: 'I would not omit that this morning Mr. Bagnall shewed me a great number of very fine original paintings, which he got by marriage with Lady Arthur, widow of Sir Daniel Arthur, a rich Irish merchant who died in Spain . . . several pieces of Monglio [*sic*], a famous painter in Spain, little known here, together with his own picture. . . .' Attention was first drawn to this passage by E. K. Waterhouse in the *Burlington Magazine*, 1947, p. 78. Presumably lot 38 in Mr. Bagnall and Lady Arthur's sale, 1757—' "Mans Head . . Morillios head by himself . . . Rembrandt" bought by Lady Cardigan for £12 12sh.'—refers to a copy of No. 6153 attributed at the sale to Rembrandt. For some light on Sir Daniel Arthur see E. K. Waterhouse, *op. cit.*, p. 78, footnote 5. It might be added that Sir Daniel paid the penalty for his services to James II, which Waterhouse describes, for his property in Ireland was forfeited during the reign of William III and Mary (see *Analecta Hibernica*, March 1930, Vol. I, p. 79). Waterhouse suggests that Sir Daniel Arthur was known to Palomino, but Palomino's reference, *op. cit.*, p. 623, to 'Francisco Artier' may appear to be more than a mere corruption of Sir Daniel's name. It should also be noted that No. 6153 does not feature in the list of Francisco Artier's collection of Murillos given by Palomino, *op. cit.*, p. 623. (**12**) 'Mr. Bagnals Soho Square . . . a Head—Moriglios own portrait—Moriglio (sold to the prince)'—Vertue's notebook, The Walpole Society, 1937–38, Vol. 26, pp. 126–7. (**13**) "In the Household Accounts of Prince Frederick and his wife, preserved in the Duchy of Cornwall Office, is an account submitted by John Anderson for work on the Prince's pictures. It was settled in September 1749, but the account for 1747 includes: 'Lineing & Cleaning Morellas Head 1:1:0'" (extract from a letter from Oliver Millar in the Gallery archives). (**14**) This reference appears in an unpublished volume of Vertue's notes, B. M., MS. 19027, f. 20 v. Information kindly provided in the letter mentioned in note 13 from Oliver Millar. (**15**) Sir Lawrence Dundas Sale, 31 May 1794 (25), sold for £105. (**16**) The National Gallery's copy of the Dundas sale catalogue contains notes by J. E. Breen. It would appear from these that Breen visited Lord Ashburnham's house in Dover Street at this date. (**17**) The Earl of Ashburnham sale, 20 July 1850 (50), sold for £829 10s. (**18**) Catalogue of Pictures at Althorp House, 1851 (272). (**19**) Science and Art Department of the Committee of the Council of Education, *List of Art Objects in the South Kensington Museum*, p. 38 (in the Victoria and Albert Museum's archives). (**20**) It should be stated that none of these engravings is exact in every detail. Palomino, *op. cit.*, p. 625, states that the other self-portrait represented the artist in a *golilla* and was owned by Don Gaspar. The engravings listed show the artist in the same clothes and with the same physiognomy as in No. 6153; for a full list see Sir William Stirling Maxwell, *Essay towards a Catologue of Prints Engraved from the works of . . . Murillo*, 1873, pp. 124–25.

NEAPOLITAN School
XVIII Century

6254 PORTRAIT OF A LADY

Oil on canvas, 30½ × 29½ (0·927 × 0·750).
Presented by Mrs. Frederick Antal in memory of her husband, 1955.

NETHERLANDISH School
XVI Century

6161 A LITTLE GIRL WITH A BASKET OF CHERRIES

Oil on canvas, 31¼ × 20½ (0·795 × 0·520).
Mrs. Charles Carstairs Bequest, 1952; entered the Collection in 1953.

GIOVANNI ANTONIO PELLEGRINI
1675–1741

Italian School; worked in Venice, in England and elsewhere in Europe.

6328   SKETCH FOR 'THE MARRIAGE OF THE ELECTOR PALATINE AND ANNA MARIA LUISA DE' MEDICI'

Oil on canvas, $17\frac{7}{8} \times 27\frac{1}{8}$ (0·454 × 0·688).
Bought out of the Annual Grant 1962.

6332   REBECCA AT THE WELL

Oil on canvas, $50\frac{1}{8} \times 41\frac{1}{8}$ (1·273 × 1·045).
Bequeathed by Claude Dickason Rotch with other pictures, 1962.

GIOVANNI BATTISTA PITTONI
1687–1767

Italian School. Born at Venice. Pupil and nephew of the mediocre Francesco Pittoni, he later came under the more fruitful influence of Sebastiano Ricci and Tiepolo, among others. Inscribed in the *Fraglia* of Venetian Painters from 1726; President of the Academy in Venice, 1758.

Pittoni produced chiefly religious and decorative pictures. In addition to the picture catalogued below there are good altarpieces by him at Sidney Sussex College, Cambridge (a 'Nativity'), and in the Edinburgh Gallery.

6279   THE NATIVITY WITH GOD THE FATHER AND THE HOLY GHOST

Oil on canvas, $87\frac{1}{2} \times 60\frac{1}{2}$ (2·227 × 1·535). Cleaned on acquisition.[1] In fair condition.

The combination of Trinity and Nativity in a single representation is unusual but by no means unprecedented; it goes back at least to the 15th century.[2] Because S. Joseph is sleeping No. 6279 has sometimes in the past been called the 'Rest on the Flight into Egypt'; but the motif of S. Joseph asleep at the Nativity again is an earlier one, found already in pictures of the 15th century. In No. 6279 both the Eternal Father and the Dove were painted over, probably in the 19th century. Since they have been found in good condition under the overpaint (see note 1), this was presumably because they were thought unsuitable.

Pittoni himself is known to have combined the two themes only this once, though he treated the subject of the Nativity often in rather similar compositions, all on a smaller scale.[3] This is his grandest treatment of his favourite theme. The altarpiece was painted probably in the early 1730's.[4]

So large a Venetian 18th-century altarpiece, painted as it is by one of the leading painters of the period who was patronised internationally, is a comparatively rare thing in England. The soft rococo colour and decorative effect explain Pittoni's popularity. In the 19th century, however, his name was apt to be ignored, and the first references to this picture (see below) attribute it wrongly to Tiepolo (*q.v.*), the most famous exponent of the Venetian rococo. The correct attribution was made by Max Goering in 1934.[5]

The picture was acquired probably by Alberic, Lord Willoughby de Eresby (d. 1870), who is known to have bought considerable quantities of Italian furniture, etc., for Grimsthorpe Castle, Lincolnshire, the family seat. It is recorded as the work of Tiepolo in an inventory of works of art at Grimsthorpe in 1865.[6] It passed to his son, the 1st Earl of Ancaster. From the 3rd Earl of Ancaster it was bought at auction, 14 May 1958, Sotheby's, lot 45, out of Grant-in-Aid and the remainders of accumulated income from the following seven Trust Funds: Champney, Waycott, Florence, Hornby-Lewis, Temple-West, Campion and Longfield Memorial, together with the assistance of the National Art-Collections Fund, the Noel Buxton Trust and sundry donations.

EXHIBITED: 1925, London, Magnasco Society, No. 23, as by Tiepolo; 1951, Whitechapel and Birmingham, *18th century Venetian Painting*, No. 92; 1954–55, Royal Academy, *European Masters of the 18th century*, No. 328; 1957, Manchester, *Art Treasures Centenary* Exhibition, No. 169.

DRAWINGS: A sheet of studies of heads in the Accademia, Venice, includes a study for S. Joseph's head, not necessarily drawn in connection with the present picture; and a sheet in a private collection, Padua, shows two studies of hands holding drapery, akin to the Virgin's right hand here. A drawing of a *putto* in the Correr Museum, Venice, is close to the *putto* in the present picture, upper right. A study for some hands in the Accademia, Venice, may be preparatory for God the Father's right hand here; cf. Pallucchini, *I Disegni di Giambattista Pittoni*, 1945, Pls. 44, 58, 64, 82. However, not all these drawings are necessarily related to No. 6279.

VERSIONS AND COPIES: Strictly speaking, there are no versions of No. 6279; the closest is a design recorded in versions in the Daniele-Folco collection in Rome (see note 3) and at Coblenz. A copy of the head of S. Joseph was in an Anonymous sale, Christie's, 10 July 1959 (lot 51).

NOTES: (**1**) The picture is reproduced before and after cleaning in the National Gallery *Report* 1958–59, Pls. 7 (black and white) and II (colour). The central part of the upper half of the canvas had been completely painted over at one time to conceal the Eternal Father and the Dove. This had involved the overpainting also of most of the sky on the left and the upper part of the globe. Before the picture was acquired, repaint had been removed from the Dove only and the obvious overpainting of much else, together with the loose condition of some of the original paint and the weakness of the support, had led to alarm concerning the structure. Relining and the removal of the overpaint resulted in a painting of perhaps more than average condition except along the top edge, where it has had to be made up. (**2**) For instance, other Persons of the Trinity are present in a 'Nativity' by Filippo Lippi in Berlin. (**3**) The following are some examples, as reproduced by Goering in *Mitteilungen des Kunsthistorischen Institutes in Florenz*, January 1934, pp. 201 ff: Rome, Daniele-Folco collection (fig. 5); Rovigo, Accademia dei Concordi (fig. 4); Folco-Zambelli-Clementi collection (fig. 3), a very different design. Another is at Munich. Yet another, as it were a detail of the central portion of the present picture, is at Budapest (published by I. Fenyö, *Acta Historiae Artium*, 1954, Vols. 3–4, p. 279, where he discusses and illustrates further examples). (**4**) The date was suggested by Goering, *loc. cit.*, p. 216; he is followed by R. Pallucchini, *I Disegni di Giambattista Pittoni*, 1945, p. 20. (**5**) Goering, *loc. cit.* (**6**) An earlier record could possibly be Tiepolo, 'The Nativity' in the sale of Sir C. Bethell Codrington deceased, Christie's, 12 May 1843, lot 72; but this is more likely to have been a sketch of some sort.

Nicolas POUSSIN
1594(?)–1665
French School; worked in Rome, and also in Paris.

6277 THE ADORATION OF THE SHEPHERDS

Oil on canvas, 38 × 29 (0·965 × 0·735). Cleaned on acquisition. In good condition.[1]

Inscribed: *N. Pusin. fe.*

An earlier episode, the Annunciation to the Shepherds, is described in the middle distance. The combination of the two scenes in one and the little band of Cherubim flying above are in the tradition of the Italian Renaissance; but the classical figure bringing an abundance of fruit in a basket is an innovation.

The picture was painted probably in the later half of the decade 1630–39; indeed it has been dated by Blunt *ca.* 1637.[2] In 1633 Poussin had painted 'The Adoration of the Magi' now at Dresden, from which some motifs are echoed in this picture: cf. the king kneeling in the foreground there and the shepherd here. This motif goes back to the 'Adoration of the Magi' of the school of Raphael in the Loggia of the Vatican, while affinity between the lower part of Poussin's composition here and Titian's woodcut of the 'Adoration of the Shepherds' is perhaps more than accidental.[3] A comparison with 'The Adoration of the Shepherds' (No. 6331) in this Exhibition, painted probably a few years earlier by his compatriot Louis Le Nain, emphasises the mastery of classical composition at which Poussin has arrived through the study of his great predecessors in Venice and in Rome.

The picture seems to have been a popular one, to judge by the existence of an engraving and the unusual number of versions and copies (see below). Who commissioned it is not known, but it might conceivably be the '*petit tableau*' of unknown subject that Poussin was sending to a M. Debonaire in April 1639,[4] though the style suggests that No. 6277 must have been painted a year or two before that date. It was possibly in the Selle sale, Paris, 1761; but the first certain record is of 1829, when it was in the collection of Sir William Procter Beauchamp at Langley Park, Norfolk.[5] There it remained until recently. In the sale of the late Commander Jocelyn Beauchamp, London, 11 July 1956 (lot 119), it was bought by D. Koetser, through whom it was acquired in 1957 out of the Temple-West Fund, with a Special Grant and with a contribution from the National Art-Collections Fund.

ENGRAVING: in reverse by Etienne Picart (1632–1711), with a dedication to Colbert (probably the elder, died 1683). It is reproduced by G. Wildenstein in his catalogue of engravings after Poussin in *Gazette des Beaux-Arts*, September–December 1955, p. 148; see also the correction by M. Davies and A. Blunt in *Gazette des Beaux-Arts*, July–August 1962, p. 210 (under W. 37).

DRAWINGS: Christ Church, Oxford, for the upper portion with the cherubs (Friedlaender, *The Drawings of Nicolas Poussin*, Vol. I, 1939, No. 35); British Museum, No. F. f. 2–163, probably *after* the lower portion, with modifications in the architecture and other small changes (Friedlaender, *op. cit.*, Vol. I, p. 19, No. A6 and Pl. 69, as Studio of Poussin).

VERSIONS AND COPIES: A version of the whole picture was in the Favier collection, Paris (catalogued by O. Grautoff, *Nicolas Poussin*, 1914, Vol. II, No. 103, as the original); a copy was in an Anonymous sale, 23 March 1927, as by Jacopo da Ponte (Friedlaender, *op. cit.*); a Spanish copy is recorded at Barcelona in 1946 (C. Sterling in *Actes du Colloque Poussin*, 1960, Vol. I, p. 276, note 8); a copy of the lower half of the composition is No. 1862 in the National Gallery (M. Davies, *National Gallery Catalogues, French School*, 2nd ed., 1957, pp. 186–87); another, similar to No. 1862, is owned by the Duke of Northumberland (Davies, *op. cit.*).

NOTES: (**1**) Except for a very slight general wearing and a single passage of deeper damage on the horizon. (**2**) Catalogue of the Exhibition Nicolas Poussin, Paris, Louvre, May–July 1960, p. 84. This date is accepted by D. Mahon in the *Gazette des Beaux-Arts*, July–August 1962, p. 103. (**3**) Reproduced by F. Mauroner, *Le Incisioni di Tiziano*, 1943, Pl. 28. (**4**) See C. Sterling in the 1960 *Poussin Exhibition Catalogue*, p. 236. (**5**) Stacey, *History of Norfolk*, 1829, Vol. II, p. 845.

REMBRANDT van Rijn
1606–1669

Dutch School; worked at Leyden and Amsterdam.

6274 AN OLD MAN IN AN ARMCHAIR, LEANING HIS HEAD ON HIS RIGHT HAND

Oil on canvas, $43\frac{5}{8} \times 34\frac{5}{8}$ ($1\cdot11 \times 0\cdot88$). Cleaned in 1962–63. In good condition.[1]

Signed and dated in the top right corner: *Rembrandt. f. | 1652*.

It has been suggested[2] that this is perhaps a reminiscence of a portrait of Tintoretto, and indeed the loose and jagged drawing of the costume in thick paint, glazed here and there with a variety of reds, together with some rather startling effects of light, recalls Tintoretto's technique at its most opulent and daring. The Gallery's *Portrait of Vincenzo Morosini* by Tintoretto (No. 4004) is not quite characteristic in its comparatively low relief; but a comparison can also be made with Titian's 'Vendramin Family' (No. 4452), which is not recorded in the Netherlands but is known to have passed from Venice to Van Dyck's collection in England between 1636 and 1641.[3] In No. 6274 the old man's fur-lined mantle is reminiscent of patrician Venetian costume. The Venetian influence, however, has in no way restricted Rembrandt's deep sympathy with the aged sitter's reflective mood.

The picture was probably among those collected by the 3rd Earl of Burlington at Chiswick House. On his death in 1753 this collection passed with the house to William, Marquess of Hartington, who in 1748 had married Charlotte Elizabeth, daughter and co-heir of the Earl and in 1755 was to become 4th Duke of Devonshire. No. 6274 was certainly in the Duke's collection at Chiswick House in 1766.[4] It was acquired from the 11th Duke of Devonshire in 1958 in part payment of estate duty, under the terms of the Finance Act, 1956.

EXHIBITED: 1837, London, British Institution, No. 55; 1876, Royal Academy, No. 243; 1898, Amsterdam, No. 85; 1899, R.A., *Rembrandt*, No. 54; 1929, R.A., *Dutch Art*, No. 126; 1938, R.A., *Seventeenth Century Art*, No. 125; 1948, London, Agnew's, *Devonshire Collection*, No. 22; 1952–53, R.A., *Dutch Pictures*, No. 172.

ENGRAVING: Mezzotint by Charles Phillips 1766 (see note 4).

NOTES: (**1**) It was relined on acquisition. The condition of the paint is good, except towards the right edge; here there are unimportant losses and a tear through the left hand. The appearance of wearing on the back of the chair and in the background above it is largely perhaps due to intentional rubbing by Rembrandt himself as the signature (mostly sound) is applied over it. (**2**) Neil MacLaren, National Gallery Catalogues, *The Dutch School*, 1960, pp. 337–38; also 'Rembrandt has here avowed more explicitly than in any other picture his acquaintance with Venetian painting'. MacLaren gives the history of the picture in full, together with the following references. He also gives as general references: J. Smith, *Catalogue Raisonné*, etc., Vol. 7, *The Life and Works of Rembrandt van Ryn*, 1836, No. 326; W. Bode and C. Hofstede de Groot, *The Complete Work of Rembrandt*, 1897–1906, No. 381; Klassiker der Kunst: *Rembrandt: Gemälde*, 1909, p. 370; Hofstede de Groot, No. 292; A. Bredius, *The Paintings of Rembrandt*, 1937, Fig. 267. (**3**) Cecil Gould, National Gallery Catalogues, *The Sixteenth Century Venetian School*, pp. 117–20. (**4**) *London and its Environs*, published by R. and J. Dodsley, 1761, already mentions two by Rembrandt in the list of pictures at Chiswick House: 'A portrait, Rembrandt' (Vol. II, p. 118) and 'A man half length, Rembrandt' (Vol. II, p. 121); but definite identification comes in 1766 with Phillips' mezzotint after the picture, of which one state is inscribed: '. . . The Studious Philosopher. From the Original Picture Painted by Rembrandt in the Collection of . . . the Duke of Devonshire at Chiswick. John Boydell excudit 1766' (J. Chaloner Smith, *British Mezzotinto Portraits*, 1883, C. Phillips No. 6).

6300 EQUESTRIAN PORTRAIT

Oil on canvas, 116 × 95 (2·945 × 2·41).

There are faint remains (best visible through infra-red photography) of a signature on the left: *R . . brandt*, and possibly of a date: *1663* (?).[1]

Cleaned on acquisition. In good condition as regards the horse and its rider. The surrounding parts are somewhat rubbed; but owing to the intended obscurity, to the sketchiness of most of the painting and to changes made by the artist, who took little or no pains to conceal them, it is difficult to say how much the picture has altered since it left his studio.

Whatever were the sitter's instructions, Rembrandt no doubt intended horse and rider to stand out from a confused, nocturnal impression. In the background on the left a coach with four occupants[2] can be discerned before a building, and perhaps a bridge, surrounded by trees.[3] In the left foreground is the prow or stern of a small boat in a stream. On the right, behind, are two men, perhaps on horseback.

As to the sitter, he wears the uniform of an officer of a civic guard.[4] His horse performs a *levade*. Attractive theories have sought to identify him with one of two members of the Amsterdam Guard of Honour which escorted Prince William of Orange during his visit to Amsterdam in 1660: either Frederick Rihel or Jacob de Graeff.[5] There are difficulties in the way of accepting either identification, though both obviously get much nearer to the sitter's identity than the traditional title of 'Marshal Turenne', to whom he bears no resemblance.[6] The date of the Prince's visit conforms not only with that which is possibly inscribed on the picture but with the style of the execution.[7] This shows Rembrandt's art in all the breadth and depth of its last decade.

One other equestrian portrait by him is known, the so-called 'Polish Rider' of the Frick collection, New York, which is perhaps not a portrait, and is much smaller and less formal. Only two pictures by Rembrandt have survived which are larger than No. 6300 in their dimensions. As an equestrian portrait on the full scale of life, it is almost unique in the history of Dutch painting.

Yet its early history is obscure, unless indeed it is the equestrian portrait of Frederick Rihel by Rembrandt mentioned in an inventory of Rihel's possessions in 1681. The objections to this identification are given in note 5. The first certain owner of No. 6300 was Count Ferdinand of Plettenberg and Wittem, with whose collection it was sold in Amsterdam in 1738.[8] Three years later it re-appeared in the sale at The Hague of G. Bicker van Zwieten.[9] 'About 1750' it was bought by the 2nd Earl Cowper.[10] In 1833 it is recorded by Passavant[11] at Panshanger, the Hertfordshire residence of the Earls Cowper, of whom the last died in 1905. It remained at Panshanger until 1953, after it had passed by inheritance from Lady Desborough to her daugher Lady Salmond. From Lady Salmond it was acquired in 1959 out of the Annual Grant and with contributions from the National Art-Collections Fund and the Pilgrim Trust, but largely by remission of estate duty and with a Special Grant.

EXHIBITED: 1815, British Institution, No. 123; 1881, Royal Academy, No. 165; 1952–53, R.A., *Dutch Pictures*, No. 270; 1953–59, Leeds, City Art Gallery; 1956, Amsterdam, Rijksmuseum, and Rotterdam, Boymans Museum, *Rembrandt*, No. 53.

ETCHED: by P. J. Arendzen.

NOTES: (1) The date was formerly often stated wrongly supposed to be 1649; see, for instance, A. Bredius, *Rembrandt Gemälde*, 1935, No. 255. (2) A drawing by Rembrandt in the British Museum is perhaps a study for the coach, see A. M. Hind, *Catalogue of Drawings by Dutch and Flemish Artists . . . in the British Museum*, 1915, Vol. I, No. 71. Hind dates this drawing 'about 1649' with which date O. Benesch, *The Drawings of Rembrandt*, 1955, Vol. 4, No. 756, agrees. Benesch, *op. cit.*, No. 728, also associates the drawing, 'Skeleton Rider', in the Hessisches Landesmuseum, Darmstadt, with No. 6300: 'The reason for Rembrandt's interest in studying the anatomical structure of a rider on horseback at the end of the 1640's must be explained in relation to the task of painting in 1649 the life-size portrait of a Cavalier on Horseback. . . .' Although No. 6300 depicts both a man on horseback and a coach, it is not necessary to associate either of these drawings directly with the picture. (3) R. van Luttervelt, *De Grote Ruiter van Rembrandt*, Nederlands Kunsthistorisch Jaarboek, 1957, No. 8, p. 189 ff., has suggested that the view in the background is of the Heiligewegspoort, Amsterdam. In view of the obscurity and sketchiness, however, such a suggestion can be no more than wish-fulfilment unless some documentary evidence is found. (4) J. G. van Gelder, 'Rembrandt and his Circle' in *The Burlington Magazine*, February 1953, p. 38. (5) It has recently been suggested by R. van Luttervelt *op. cit.*, pp. 193 ff., that the sitter is Jacob de Graeff, cornet of the Amsterdam guard of honour which escorted Prince William of Orange during his visit to Amsterdam in 1660 and that the scene depicts a section of the guard of honour—part of de Graeff's troop—with Prince William's coach in the background as it passed outside the Heiligewegspoort. This theory is difficult to accept not merely because the sitter does not carry the pennant which, as we are shown in a contemporary engraving of this guard of honour (A. van Stolk, *Verzameling*, 1897, Vol. II, No. 2285), was carried by the cornet Jacob de Graeff—Rembrandt was a wilful painter—but because the age of the rider appears to be much more than eighteen—Jacob de Graeff's age in 1660 (see Luttervelt, *op. cit.*, p. 206). Although E. Michel, *Rembrandt his Life*, etc. . . . , 1894, Vol. II, p. 17, stated that Bredius felt that the sitter was younger than thirty-eight; W. Bode and C. Hofstede de Groot, *The Complete Work of Rembrandt*, Vol. 5, 1901, pp. 24–25, stated that the sitter looked 'barely thirty', he does not in fact look any younger than the youngest sitter in, for instance, the 'Staalmeesters' (Rijksmuseum No. 2017), who is *ca.* 33. A second theory, proposed by A. Bredius, 'Rembrandtiana' in *Oud-Holland*, 1910, pp. 193–95, is that the sitter is Frederick Rihel, since an inventory of 1681 of his possessions mentions an equestrian portrait of him by Rembrandt. Frederick Rihel was also probably a member of the 1660 guard of honour and was about thirty-five years old at this time, see I. H. van Eegen, *Frederick Rihel een 17de Eeuwse Zakenman en Paardenliefhebber*, Amstelodanum, April 1958, pp. 73 ff. But he was not an officer at this time, see R. van Luttervelt, *Frederick Rihel of Jacob de Graeff*, Amstelodanum, September 1958, pp. 147 ff. It certainly has not been proved that the scene depicted in the background has any reference to Prince William of Orange during his visit to Amsterdam in 1660. The evidence provided by the inventory, published by Bredius, is insufficient as evidence alone, and for these reasons it is felt that the sitter must still remain anonymous. J. G. van Gelder's suggestion, *loc. cit.*, that the coat of arms on the breaststrap might lead to the identification of the sitter cannot be followed up as it seems unlikely that a coat of arms was ever intended; certainly it is impossible to read it as such. (**6**) Given in the sale of 1738. The lack of facial resemblance was pointed out by Bode and Hofstede de Groot, *loc. cit.* (**7**) As suggested by H. Honour, An Equestrian Portrait by Rembrandt, *Leeds Art Calendar*, Summer, 1953, pp. 7–8; with whom J. G. van Gelder agreed in a letter, Dutch Pictures at the Royal Academy, *Burlington Magazine*, December 1953, p. 393; see also R. van Luttervelt, *De Grote Ruiter van Rembrandt*, Nederlands Kunsthistorisch Jaarboek, 1957, No. 8, pp. 211 ff. (**8**) Sold on 2 April 1738, lot 130, 88 florins, see G. Hoet, *Catalogus . . . van Schilderyen*, 1752, Vol. I, p. 505. (**9**) G. Bicker van Zwieten sale, The Hague, 12 April 1741, lot 129, 90 florins, see G. Hoet, *op. cit.*, 1752, Vol. II, p. 21. (**10**) See H. Honour, *op. cit.*, p. 7 and footnote 3. M. L. Boyle, *Biographical Catalogue of the Portraits at Panshanger*, 1885, p. 38, stated that this picture was sold from a private collection in Amsterdam in 1740 (see also J. Smith, *Catalogue Raissonné*, etc., Part 7, *The Life and Works of Rembrandt van Rhjn*, 1836, No. 323), and bought by the Earl of Grantham. This may have been a mistaken reference to the Bicker van Zwieten sale (see note 9); there is no indication that the Earl of Grantham ever owned the picture. (**11**) J. D. Passavant, *Kunstreise durch England und Belgien*, 1833, p. 100. See also Waagen, *Treasures of Art in Great Britain*, 1854, Vol. III, p. 16, and C. Hofstede de Groot, *A Catalogue Raisonné*, etc., Vol. 6, *Rembrandt*, etc., 1916, No. 772.

Guido RENI
1575–1642
Italian School; worked at Bologna and in Rome.

6270   THE ADORATION OF THE SHEPHERDS

Oil on canvas, 189 × 126 (4·800 × 3·210).
Bought out of the Annual Grant and the Florence Fund in 1957.

Pierre-Auguste RENOIR
1841–1919
French School; worked in Paris.

6319   BAIGNEUSE SE COIFFANT

Oil on canvas, $15\frac{1}{2} \times 11\frac{1}{2}$ (0·394 × 0·292).
Signed: *Renoir*.
During the 1870's, when he was most actively participating in the Impressionists' experiments in the break-up of outline under the impact of light, Renoir

had painted few nudes. His journey to Italy in 1881, made at a time when he realised that he, at least, could go no farther in Impressionism, greatly stimulated the affinity that he must always have felt with classical art and led him to put emphasis again on contour. One of the results was a series of nudes, and for the rest of his life the nude remained his favourite subject-matter. No. 6319 admirably illustrates his figure-painting in the second half of the '80's.

The picture was on the London art market in 1934 as from the collection of Franz Georg, Reims. Later it was in the collection of Sir Chester Beatty. It was presented by Sir Antony and Lady Hornby, 1961.

EXHIBITED: June 1934, London, Lefevre Gallery, No. 27; 1955–61, National Gallery, with other pictures from the Chester Beatty collection.

6306 PORTRAIT OF MADAME EDWARDS

Oil on canvas, $36\frac{1}{4} \times 28\frac{3}{4}$ (0·921 × 0·73). Apparently in excellent condition.
Signed and dated: *Renoir '04*.

In the preceding year the sitter had married Alfred Edwards. She was born Godebska and had previously been married to Thadée Natanson, founder of the *Revue Blanche*. Her third husband was the Spanish painter, José-Maria Sert, and it is as Misia Sert that she is chiefly remembered. Under this name she published her memoirs (English translation 1953).[1] She moved in the society of *avant-garde* artists in Paris from about the turn of the present century and was portrayed by many of them. She was an early patron of Diaghilev. In her memoirs the sitter speaks of seven or eight portraits that Renoir did of her, each requiring three whole-day sittings per week for at least a month. Two portraits other than the present one are in the Barnes Foundation, Merion, Pa., and (formerly) in the collection of Ralph M. Coe, Cleveland, Ohio.

The picture was apparently retained by the sitter in her possession until some time during the Second War.[2] Later it was in the collection of Walter P. Chrysler. It was sold with other pictures from the Chrysler collection, Sotheby's, 1 July 1959. It was bought from a private collector through Arthur Tooth & Son in August 1960 out of Grant-in-Aid.

EXHIBITED: 1943, Paris, Charpentier, *Scènes et Figures Parisiennes*, 1958, New York, Wildenstein, *Renoir* Exhibition, No. 58.

NOTES: (1) *Two or Three Muses*, 1953 (translated by Moura Budberg). Unfortunately the authoress admits to being vague and was elderly at the time of writing. It is therefore unwise to take her statements *au pied de la lettre*. No. 6306 may or may not be the picture which she describes Renoir as painting on pp. 82–84. (2) Baroness Budberg, in an oral communication, remembers the picture in the sitter's possession in the 1930's.

6317 LA DANSEUSE AU TAMBOURIN

6318 LA DANSEUSE AUX CASTAGNETTES

Oil on canvas, each $61 \times 25\frac{1}{2}$ (1·55 × 0·648). Apparently in perfect condition.
Each signed and dated: *Renoir. 09*.

The two pictures were painted in the summer of 1909 in Paris for the dining-room of an apartment at 24, Avenue de Friedland there.[1] Renoir's first idea was that the girls should be bearing dishes of fruit, but he abandoned this in case the family might move house and might wish to hang the pictures in some room other than the dining-room—as in due course they did. The original setting was on either side of a large mirror which overhung the fireplace.[2] In their final form the *Danseuses* thus became a kind of free-moving pictorial caryatids; two pictures of rather similar form, now in the Barnes Foundation, Merion, Pa., actually represent caryatids.[3] Renoir is perhaps best known in England as an Impressionist painter of the contemporary scene; but he was early conscious of the limitations of Impressionism and sought a more classical mould for his forms. As painters of the Renaissance did with antique sculptures, he made studies from the work of French sculptors of classical periods in order to 'correct' his modelling of the nude. Innumerable sculptured caryatids were of course to hand, especially on the exterior and interior of the Louvre.

The head of '*La Danseuse aux castagnettes*' was modelled by Madame Renoir's cousin Gabrielle Renard, who, besides being his customary model, was first nursemaid to the young Jean Renoir, then housekeeper and finally nurse to the invalid painter himself. Renoir was already suffering from arthritis and these have been said to be the last pictures which he painted standing up.[4] The model for the figure in that picture and for the whole of '*La Danseuse au tambourin*' was Madame Georgette Pigeot, who in 1961 gave much valuable information concerning the painting of the pictures. She confirmed the account of herself given by the painter's son, Jean Renoir:[5] 'She posed a great deal for Renoir. She was a dressmaker, and, being highly skilled, she earned a good living. I think she posed for him because she liked being with him. To my father's great delight, she sang all the time, and kept him up-to-date on all the latest songs in the café-concerts.' Mme. Pigeot remembers going with Renoir to buy the slippers which she wore for these occasions; part of the *torero* costume worn for the sittings is now in the Renoir house, near Cagnes, which has been preserved by the Fondation Renoir.

The apartment for which the pictures were painted belonged to Maurice Gangnat, Renoir's most liberal and discerning patron at this period. Jean Renoir writes of him:[6] 'That great bourgeois gentleman was carrying on the tradition of old Choquet. His feeling for painting was astounding. Whenever he entered the studio, his gaze always fell immediately on the canvas Renoir considered his best. "He has an eye for it"! my father declared. Renoir also said that collectors who really know anything are rarer than good painters.'

The painter is recorded as placing these two pictures very high on the list of his productions,[7] and they are regarded by authorities on his works as among the most important of his fully developed style.[8]

At the sale of Maurice Gangnat's collection in Paris in 1925 each fetched a higher bid than was made for any of the 158 other pictures by Renoir. They were bought in by his son Philippe Gangnat, and therefore remained with the family until they were acquired by the National Gallery. From Monsieur Philippe Gangnat they were bought in 1961 from the Annual Grant but mostly with a Special Grant from the Exchequer.

EXHIBITED: 1931, Paris, *Exposition Coloniale*; 1933, Paris, Orangerie, *Renoir*, Nos. 118 and 119; 1937, London, Rosenberg and Helft, Nos. 13 and 14; 1937–54, Philadelphia Museum of Art; 1955, Paris, Durand-Ruel, *Renoir, Collection Maurice Gangnat* (in aid of the Fondation Renoir, of which M. Philippe Gangnat is President), Nos. 41 and 42.

DRAWINGS: Renoir's drawings *à la sanguine* for both pictures were shown at the Reid Gallery, London, in 1961.

NOTES: (1) Letter in the Gallery archives from Monsieur Philippe Gangnat. (2) Oral statements by M. Philippe Gangnat and Mme. Pigeot (see subsequent text). (3) For these see J. Meier-Graefe, *Renoir*, 1929 ed., Leipzig, Pl. 292 and p. 399, and Albert C. Barnes and Violette de Mazia, *The Art of Renoir*, 1959, p. 330; Meier-Graefe dates them 1901, Barnes and de Mazia *ca.* 1910. (4) M. Philippe Gangnat. (5) Jean Renoir, *Renoir, My Father*, English translation, 1962, p. 397. (6) Jean Renoir, *op. cit.*, p. 397. He also writes, p. 148: ' "We don't work [Renoir stated] for the critics, or for the dealers, or even for art-lovers in general; but only for the half-dozen or so painters who are competent to judge our efforts because they paint themselves." As this last assertion seemed too positive, he added, "We paint also for Monsieur Choquet, for Gangnat, and for the unknown man in the street who stops in front of an art-dealer's window and gets two minutes' pleasure from looking at one of our pictures".' (7) Letter of 3 February 1962 in the Gallery archives from the artist's son Claude Renoir: '. . . mon *Père* . . . *leur accordait une toute première place dans son œuvre*'. (8) *E.g.*, by Meier-Graefe, *Renoir*, 1912 ed., pp. 176–78. He begins his discussion of the pictures: '*Dans la masse énorme de ses tableaux, une œuvre depasse les autres et peut passer pour le point d'aboutissement de certaines tendances du maître. Elle se compose de deux panneaux formant pendant et représentant des danseuses . . . jamais l'art de Renoir ne fut plus frais et plus joyeux.*' Also Paul Jamot in *Gazette des Beaux-Arts*, 1923, period V, Vol. 8, p. 329: '*deux panneaux décoratifs qui comptent parmi ses œuvres le plus puissantes*'.

SALVATOR ROSA
1615–1673

Italian School; worked in Naples, Rome and Florence.

6298 LANDSCAPE, WITH TOBIAS AND THE ANGEL

Oil on canvas, 58 × 88 (1·473 × 2·235).
Bought out of the Annual Grant in 1959.

SALOMON VAN RUYSDAEL
1600/3(?)–1670

Dutch School; worked at Haarlem.

6338 A VIEW OF DEVENTER

Oil on oak, 20⅜ × 30⅛ (0·518 × 0·765).
Signed and dated: *S V R · 1657* (VR in monogram).
Presented by William Edward Brandt, Henry Augustus Brandt, Walter Augustus Brandt and Alice Marie Bleecker in memory of Rudolph Ernst Brandt, 1962.

Bernardo STROZZI
1581–1644

Italian School. Born at Genoa and early trained as a painter. At seventeen he entered the Franciscan Order, hence his nickname *il Prete Genovese* (see under No. 6321). He received temporary permission to leave the cloister, but fled eventually from Genoa in or about 1630 to Venice, where he settled until his death. His work was much influenced by Rubens (who had worked in Genoa in the first decade of the 17th century) and increasingly by Venetian art after his arrival in Venice. His portraits and religious and genre pictures were of considerable importance for the evolution of Venetian painting right into the 18th century.

6321 AN ALLEGORY OF FAME

Oil on canvas, 42 × 59¾ (1·067 × 1·517). Cleaned on acquisition. In good condition.[1]

The girl holds up a golden trumpet, while she rests a larger one, perhaps of baser metal, perhaps of wood. These probably indicate the ambiguous aspect of fame, which was a theme of Antiquity.

There were pictures by Rubens and van Dyck in Strozzi's native Genoa, and even the Dutch painter Lastman (*q.v.*), who was in Italy at the beginning of the 17th century, might be cited as possibly providing some of the northern elements which are blended with Italian in his hybrid but individual style. The picture was painted probably in the 1630's.[2] By this time Strozzi had settled in Venice, and the picture is a prelude to some developments of the later 17th and 18th centuries among Venetian painters. It is not altogether surprising therefore that it was attributed at one time to Tiepolo. The correct attribution first was made apparently by Borenius.[3]

The picture is possibly the *Fama del prete genovese* recorded in 1709 at Venice in the inventory of Ferdinando Carlo Gonzaga, last Duke of Mantua.[4] During the 1930's No. 6321 was in an English private collection. It was bought in 1961 from Malcolm Waddingham out of the Grant-in-Aid, with contributions from the Temple-West, Clarke, Florence and Hornby-Lewis Funds.

NOTES: (1) The canvas was relined. There were many small losses in the background of the painting and a very few on the figure. See also note 3, below. (2) L. Mortari in *Paragone*, Sept., 1962, pp. 26–27, dates it in the later part of the decade. (3) Information kindly provided by Mr. Waddingham. (4) Cf. A. Luzio *La Galleria dei Gonzaga ...*, 1913, p. 318. That picture measured 6 × 9 *quarte* (ca. 54 × 81 inches) and was therefore larger than No. 6321; but it is not hard to believe that this has been reduced in size. No other painting of the subject by Strozzi is known.

Giambattista TIEPOLO
1696–1770

Italian School. Worked in his native Venice and in other cities of northern Italy. In 1750–53 at Würzburg; in 1762–70 in Madrid, where he died.

6273 THE TRINITY APPEARING TO S. CLEMENT (?)

Oil on canvas, $27\frac{1}{4} \times 21\frac{3}{4}$ (0·692 × 0·552). Apparently in perfect condition.

A disciple of SS. Peter and Paul, S. Clement was, according to the tradition of the Roman Church, the third Bishop of Rome; and he is considered as one of the Fathers of the Church. That he is the subject here is suggested by the picture's origin.

This is the *modello* for Tiepolo's altarpiece now in the Alte Pinakothek at Munich.[1] The altarpiece comes from the chapel (destroyed in the 1939–45 War) of the nuns of Notre Dame at Nymphenburg and was probably commissioned by the Archbishop-Elector of Cologne, Clemens August, a brother of the Bavarian Elector and a great patron of the day. He perpetuated the name of Clement in various foundations and is likely to have chosen his namesake Pope Clement I as the subject for the altarpiece. He was incidentally the protégé of Pope Clement XI. He visited Venice more than once but had no other work by Tiepolo among his pictures.

The style of *modello* and altarpiece suggests a date in the decade of 1730–39, probably in the earlier half.[2] At this period Clemens August was commissioning altarpieces from Tiepolo's older contemporaries in Venice, Piazzetta and Giovanni Pittoni (*q.v.*), while Tiepolo himself was beginning to establish an international reputation. He is likely to have submitted the *modello* to such a patron for approval. It is more than a sketch; indeed its highly finished quality and brilliant colour effect make it something out of the ordinary run of working sketches or even *modelli*. This perhaps accounts for the existence of two versions (see below).

The *modello* itself had been presumed lost and was first published on its acquisition in 1957.[3] It was possibly in an anonymous sale at Lepke's, Berlin, 11 February 1913, lot 131 (Venetian 18th century, 'S. Gregory before the Trinity').[4] Later it was in a private collection in New York. No. 6273 was purchased from Julius Weitzner out of the Champney, Clarke, Florence, Hornby-Lewis and Temple-West Funds, with the aid of the National Art-Collections Fund.

VERSIONS: New York, Metropolitan Museum of Art; another in a private collection there.

NOTES: (**1**) First published by M. Goering in *Pantheon*, 1944, p. 18. (**2**) A. Morassi, *A Complete Catalogue of the Paintings of G. B. Tiepolo*, 1962, p. 16, dates it about 1734–37. (**3**) See M. Levey in the *Burlington Magazine*, Vol. XCIX, 1957, p. 256 ff. (**4**) Lot 130 of this sale, also called Venetian 18th century, was *S. Elizabeth of Hungary*, Pittoni's composition executed as an altarpiece at Mergentheim and commissioned by the Archbishop-Elector.

6302 TWO ORIENTALS STANDING

Oil on canvas, $63\frac{1}{4} \times 21\frac{1}{2}$ (1·656 × 0·546). The measurements of the three pictures following, Nos. 6303–05, are the same. Nos. 6302–04 are apparently in good condition except along the edges, which are made up in varying degrees. The condition of No. 6305 is less certain.

At the feet of the two old men is a shield, in design much like that of one of the warriors in No. 6303; but there is not necessarily any but a decorative connection between the two compositions.

All four pictures obviously make up a decorative series, and they are all, as it were, caprice variations on themes dear to Tiepolo; but there is only one specific subject, that from Tasso of Rinaldo looking in the magic mirror (No. 6303). This theme often occurs in his work, notably among the frescoes of 1757 in the Villa Valmarana, near Vicenza.[1] The series probably dates from much the same time, the later part of the decade of 1750–59.[2] Giambattista Tiepolo's authorship of three-quarters of the present series is patent; moreover, Nos. 6302–04 were etched as his work by his sons, two compositions by Domenico and one by Lorenzo Tiepolo.[3] No. 6305, which was not etched, is weaker as well as more damaged, and is perhaps best thought of as only a production of the studio.

Nothing is known of any commission and the history of the series is unknown until the 19th century. It was probably in the sale of Samuel, Graf von Festetits, Vienna, 11 April and 2 May 1859, mounted as two pictures (lots 104 and 105). Formed into a single screen, the four pictures were in the Friedrich von Rosenberg sale, Vienna, 9 April 1883 (lot 352). In 1902 they are recorded in the collection of Baroness Willy Rothschild at Frankfurt. Recently they were in the collection of Madame de Becker, New York. They were bought in 1960 from Messrs. Rosenberg and Stiebel, New York, out of the Annual Grant-in-Aid.

6303 RINALDO LOOKING IN THE MAGIC MIRROR

The subject is from Tasso's *Gerusalemme Liberata*, Canto XVI, v. 30, where Rinaldo, who has been under the spell of Armida, sees his reflection in the shield and is ashamed of his effeminate appearance. He is throwing down the garland of flowers seen at the lower right. In the background are the warriors Carlo and Ubaldo sent to rescue him from Armida.

6304 A SEATED MAN AND A GIRL WITH A PITCHER

6305 TWO ORIENTALS UNDER A PINE-TREE

See under No. 6302.

EXHIBITED: 1934, Amsterdam, '*Italiaansche Kunst in Nederlandsch Bezit*', No. 359 (reproduced in the catalogue), lent anonymously.

NOTES: (1) Cf. R. Pallucchini, *Gli Affreschi di Giambattista e Giandomenico Tiepolo alla villa Valmarana . . .*, 1945, Pl. 66. (2) A. Morassi, *A Complete Catalogue of the Paintings of G. B. Tiepolo*, 1962, p. 17, dates them *ca.* 1750–55. (3) Nos. 6302 and 6304 were etched by Domenico Tiepolo; No. 6303 by Lorenzo Tiepolo. See A. de Vesme, *Le Peintre-Graveur Italien*, 1906, pp. 428 (Nos. 110, 111) and 442 (No. 5). (4) This and the previous provenance quoted by H. Modern, *Giovanni Battista Tiepolo*, 1902, p. 54.

PAOLO UCCELLO

ca. 1397–1475

Paolo di Dono, called *Uccello*. Italian School; worked in Florence.

6294 S. GEORGE AND THE DRAGON

Oil on canvas, $22\frac{1}{4} \times 29\frac{1}{4}$ (0·565 × 0·74). Cleaned on acquisition. In good condition.[1]

In the mid-15th century oil-paintings on canvas were perhaps not so rare as may have been supposed; but very few indeed from this early period have survived.[2]

Though noteworthy for the finish of the composition and the precision of the execution, this picture has many *pentimenti* (changes in design, which have become apparent with the increased transparency of the paint). Thus the level of the ground has been raised, the cave having at one time descended much lower on the left, and the mats of herbage on it have also been partly re-arranged. The hands of the Princess were once in a different position, and larger, with the girdle in her left hand instead of the right; her crown was originally at a steeper angle. A curved mark across the lower part of her dress has not been explained. The massed clouds on the right partly cover a continuation of the trees.

The story of S. George and the dragon has been told with many variations; but the standard version is in *The Golden Legend* by the 13th-century Dominican, Jacopus de Voragine, which was very popular in the 15th century. According to this author the dragon lived in a lake, of which Uccello shows only a corner at the back of the cave. It is fed by a trickle of water from a spring in the rock wall behind the princess' head. The dragon was the terror of the city on the distant hill and every day issued forth to receive its tribute in kind: at first two sheep but later, when mutton was scarce, one sheep and one human. Finally, the lot fell upon the King's daughter; but S. George arrived in time to save her. He wounded the dragon with his lance, whereupon the Princess put her girdle round the dragon's neck and it followed her 'as it had been a meek beast and debonair' (trans. Caxton). The three went into the city, where the King and all the people were baptised. S. George then killed the dragon with his sword. The picture shows the attack by S. George with his lance. But the next incident is also adumbrated, for the tranquil Princess has put her girdle round the dragon's neck, although (by some whim or carelessness) she continues to wear another girdle. In the sky a vortex at the end of a spiral of cloud seems to direct S. George's lance; the figure of God does not appear, as in some pictures, the miracle being expressed merely as a disturbance of nature.[3] As in several small pictures by Uccello, there is a crescent moon.

The costume and the hair-style of the Princess make it possible to date the picture about 1460.[4]

A picture on panel ascribed to Uccello, showing the same subject but differing considerably in composition, is in the Musée Jacquemart-André in Paris.[5] It was lent to the National Gallery from December 1961 until February 1962, when the two pictures were hung together.

Unrecorded until 1898, when Charles Loeser published it[6] as the work of Uccello, and probably never publicly exhibited, No. 6294 was perhaps not much studied in the original until its acquisition by the National Gallery. Some doubts about the attribution had from time to time been expressed; indeed the opinions of the critics on which pictures in Uccello's style are by Uccello himself have

6—A.C.

varied considerably; but the doubts seem by no means justified, especially since the cleaning.[7]

The late owner believes that the picture was bought by his father Count Karl Lanckoronski, before 1898, probably in northern Italy.[8] It was removed from the Lanckoronski Palace in Vienna in 1945 without a frame and was not hung again until it reached the National Gallery. It was bought from Count Antoine Lanckoronski in Zürich in 1959 out of the Annual Grant and with a Special Grant from the Exchequer, with contributions also from the Phillott and Temple-West Funds (see Preface, p. x).

NOTES: (**1**) The canvas has been cut at the left and probably at the foot, but, to judge by the composition, not by very much. The paint is in good condition, although worn in places. The spring in the side of the cave feeding the pool there was revealed by the cleaning. Old overpainting was removed from the vortex in the sky. (**2**) There is no reason to suppose that the painting has been transferred from panel; for this and other technical points see N. S. Brommelle (who cleaned the picture in the National Gallery) in *The Museums Journal*, July 1959, pp. 87–95. (**3**) See Martin Davies in *The Burlington Magazine*, September–October 1959, Vol. CI, p. 309 ff., for comments on various details of the iconography. (**4**) Note by Stella Mary Pearce in the N.G. archives. (**5**) John Pope-Hennessy, *Paolo Uccello*, 1950, Pl. 69. (**6**) Loeser in the *Repertorium für Kunstwissenschaft*, 1898, pp. 88–89. (**7**) Loeser's attribution to Uccello was followed in 1901 by Berenson, *The Florentine Painters of the Renaissance*, 2nd edition, p. 140, and again in the 3rd edition, 1909, p. 186. A. Venturi, *Storia dell'Arte Italiana*, Vol. VII, Part I, 1911, p. 340, attributed this and other pictures to an unknown cassone painter. Schubring, *Cassoni*, 1923, p. 240, van Marle, *The Development of the Italian Schools of Painting*, Vol. X, 1928, p. 207, and L. Venturi in *L'Arte*, Vol. XXXIII, 1930, p. 63, again attributed No. 6294 to Uccello. In 1932 Berenson, *Italian Pictures of the Renaissance*, p. 342, changed his mind and attributed it to the mediocre Giovanni di Francesco, the 'Master of the Carrand Triptych', under whose name he grouped an extensive miscellany of pictures. This led Pudelko, in *Das siebente Jahrzehnt: Festschrift zum 70. Geburtstag von Adolph Goldschmidt*, 1935, p. 127, to attempt a further grouping of many of these pictures, including No. 6294, round an 'Adoration' at Karlsruhe. Salmi, *Paolo Uccello, Andrea del Castagno, Domenico Veneziano*, 1938, Pl. 20, has attributed No. 6294 to Uccello and an assistant; Boeck, *Paolo Uccello*, 1939, p. 116, Pope-Hennessy, *The Complete Work of Paolo Uccello*, 1950, pp. 23 and 152, and Enio Sindona, *Paolo Uccello*, 1957, p. 62, have declared in favour of Uccello himself. See also John Pope-Hennessy in *The Manchester Guardian*, 28 January 1959, and Philip Hendy in the *Listener*, 4 February 1960, pp. 228–29. The picture has been much discussed by various writers; the references given here are far from complete. (**8**) Information supplied orally by the late owner in 1958.

Diego VELÁZQUEZ

1599–1660

Spanish School; worked in Seville and Madrid, also in Italy.

6264 S. JOHN ON THE ISLAND OF PATMOS

Oil on canvas, 53¼ × 40¼ (1·355 × 1·022). Cleaned in 1946. In fair condition, but somewhat worn in the sky. The marks showing light below the eagle's feet and to the right of the tree are casual brushstrokes on the canvas priming, which now show through as the paint has become more translucent with time. This phenomenon is so characteristic of Velázquez as to amount almost to a signature, though his habit is not always as conspicuous as it is here.

On the island of Patmos S. John the Evangelist, attended by his emblematic eagle, is writing the Apocalypse. The vivid light comes from his vision in the night sky, over the dark sea. Here side by side are 'a woman clothed with the sun, and the moon under her feet' and a winged dragon with two heads and a ring of stars round his two tails, a simplification, presumably, of the 'great red dragon, having seven heads and ten horns' whose 'tail drew the third part of the stars of heaven and did cast them to the earth'. The dragon here is submissive, and the woman is wearing 'the two wings of the great eagle' given to her after the dragon himself had been cast down to the earth from Heaven (*The Revelation of S. John the Divine*, XII, vv. 1–17).

Of all the saints S. John Evangelist has the closest relationship with the Virgin, who was entrusted to his care; and this picture has probably from the first had as companion 'The Immaculate Conception' by Velázquez. The latter has many miniature symbols and is virtually identical in size.[1]

The figure of S. John is painted with all Velázquez' perspicuous observation. There is some broad resemblance in pose in a drawing of the same subject dated 6 September 1632 in the British Museum by his master and father-in-law Francisco Pacheco;[2] and the suggestion has been made that Velázquez and Pacheco made use of a common source.[3] A drawing of S. Mark of the same year by Pacheco in the Witt collection, Courtauld Institute, may also have some connection with No. 6264.[4] No exact source has been found. The general idea of S. John represented as a young man, accompanied by his eagle, writing his book on a miniature island is commonly found in northern painting of the 15th and early 16th centuries. Charming examples in the National Gallery Reference Section are Nos. 4901, South German School, 15th century, and 717, from the Studio of the Early Netherlandish 'Master of the Female Half Lengths'. Pacheco wrote some twenty years after No. 6264 was painted that S. John on Patmos should be represented as an old man; he criticised Dürer for rendering him as a young man,[5] and it is possible that Velázquez may have been inspired by Dürer's example.[6] Velázquez was at least obeying his teacher when he dressed the Saint in white with a red mantle.[7] The woman of the Apocalypse and the dragon may have been inspired by an engraving by Juan de Jáuregui.[8] Velázquez, perhaps for the first time, has rendered the whole as a night scene in accordance with the idea of S. John's vision and out of his admiration in these years for Caravaggio and other *tenebrosi*.

The suggestion that S. John is a self-portrait[9] by Velázquez is not convincing, particularly in view of the angle of the head.[10] The resemblance is only superficial with the supposed self-portrait in the Prado Museum (No. 1224), which many have difficulty in reconciling with the much later authentic self-portrait in '*Las Meninas*'.[11] The model for the S. John quite possibly re-appears in profile in Velázquez' 'S. Thomas' at Orléans and in the genre scene with men eating and drinking in Budapest.[12]

Unanimously considered as an early work,[13] No. 6264 is close in style to 'The Immaculate Conception' and both were probably painted as early as 1617–18,[14] certainly before Velázquez paid a first short visit in 1622 to Madrid from his native Seville. They were painted probably for the wealthy convent of the Carmelitas Calzados at Seville, in the chapter house of which they are first recorded in 1800.[15] From the convent they were bought probably in 1809 by Canon López Cepero, then Dean of Seville, who formed a great collection. He sold them that year to Bartholomew Frere, who was *ad interim* Minister Plenipotentiary at Seville for a few months in 1809–10.[16] He was nephew of the statesman, Bartle Frere. Bartholomew Frere did not retire from foreign service until 1821; but the pictures were in England before 1813.[17] He died in 1851, and they seem to have been stored for a great many years before they devolved upon Laurie Frere, of Twyford House, Bishops Stortford.[8] The two pictures were lent to the National Gallery in 1945 by Mrs. P. Woodall and the Misses Frere. 'The Immaculate Conception' is still on loan. No. 6264 was purchased from the executors of Laurie Frere with the aid of a Special Grant and contributions from the Pilgrim Trust and the National Art-Collections Fund in 1956.

EXHIBITED: 1910, London, R.A., Burlington Fine Arts Club, No. 47; 1947, National Gallery, Arts Council, *Spanish Pictures*, No. 26; 1960, Madrid, '*Velázquez y lo Velázqueño*', No. 31.

NOTES: (**1**) The two pictures have hung as pendants in the National Gallery from 1945 until the opening of the present Exhibition, and it is hoped that this will continue after it is closed. For the two pictures see Carl Justi, *Velázquez y su siglo*, trans. P. Marrades, 1953, pp. 138–42. 'The Immaculate Conception' is reproduced on p. 139. (**2**) Inscribed: *6 de setiembre de 1632* and *Fco Pacheco*. Reproduced, T. Borenius, 'Drawings in the Collection of Mr. A. G. B. Russell', in *The Connoisseur*, Vol. 66, 1923, p. 8, No. IX; E. du Gué Trapier, *Notes on Spanish Drawings*, in *Notes Hispanic*, Hispanic Society of America, 1941, fig. 10 and p. 15, suggests that this and the S. Mark (see 4 below) are studies for a lost predella by Pacheco. (**3**) See Trapier, *Velázquez*, 1948, p. 43. D. Angulo Iñíguez, *Cinco Nuevos Cuadros de Zurbarán* in *Archivo Español de Arte*, Vol. XVII, 1944, p. 2, suggested that while the general conception was Pacheco's he was in this instance influenced by Velázquez. The same author, '*Velázquez y Pacheco*', *Arch. Esp. de Arte*, Vol. XXIII, 1950, p. 355, discussing the relation between Velázquez' 'Immaculate Conception' and Pacheco's (private collection Madrid), suggested that it was possible that Velázquez may have used an earlier drawing by Pacheco which Pacheco himself used later, but that more probably an engraving was the common source. This could be what happened here. (**4**) Courtauld Institute of Art, Witt collection, No. 1481; inscribed: *23 de octobre de 1632*; reproduced in A. L. Mayer '*Los Dibujos de la colección Witt en Londres*', in *Arte Español*, Vol. 8, 1926–27, opp. p. 2. Mayer states that this drawing showed Pacheco's declining powers as a draughtsman. (**5**) '*En todas estas istorias* (S. John writing the Apocalypse) *se a depintar Anciano, i venerable. No se que movió al gran Alberto Durero a pintarlo moço en su Apocalipsi, no lo hizo así el doctísmo Luis del Alcaçar . . .*', F. Pacheco, *Arte de la Pintura*, 1649, p. 561. Pacheco would have seen a version of Dürer's 'Apocalypse' in 1611 at the Escorial, see Pacheco, *op. cit.*, pp. 461–62. (**6**) C. Justi, *op. cit.*, p. 142, draws attention to the engravings by Jan Sadeler after Martin de Vos in this context. (**7**) Pacheco, *op. cit.*, p. 561: '*Pintesse cõ tunica ceñida i manto, la cual yo pinto siempre blãca por su pureza: i el mãto roxo*'. D. Angulo Iñíguez in *Arch. Esp. de Arte*, Vol. XVII, 1944, p. 2, footnote 1, stated: '*No siguió, en cambio, Velázquez las ideas de su maestro en cuanto al manto, pues lo pintó de violeta en lugar de rojo, como aquél aconsejaba*'. However the connection seems close enough to be mentioned; as Trapier pointed out, *Velázquez*, 1948, p. 47, Velázquez in part followed the precepts of his teacher in his dated 'Adoration of the Kings' at the Prado (No. 1166). (**8**) See Trapier, *op. cit.*, p. 38, and note 5. The engraving was for Luis de Alcázar's '*Vestigatio Arcani Sensus Apocalypse*', etc., Antwerp 1614; it is reproduced in Miguel Herrero, '*Jáuregui como dibujante*', *Arte Español*, Vol. 3, 1941, opp. p. 12. (**9**) See J. Allende-Salazar, *Velázquez*, Klassiker der Kunst, 1925, p. 273. (**10**) C. Pemán, *Sobre Autorretratos de Juventud de Velázquez*, *Varia Velazqueña*, 1960, Vol. I, p. 699: '*La ulterior comparación que Allende-Salazar sostuve* con el modelo para el San Juan en Patmos [sic] . . . no es concluyente ni por parecido suficiente ni por el hecho de que el San Juan mira en una dirección en que un pintor no puede verse a sí mismo a no ser mediante un complicado juego de espejos'. (11) Trapier, op. cit., p. 38, says that the facial type never recurred. But N. MacLaren, An Exhibition of Spanish Paintings, Arts Council, 1947, No. 26, suggests the basic list. J. Pruvost-Auzas, L'Apôtre Saint Thomas de Velázquez au Musée des Beaux-Arts d'Orléans, Varia Velazqueña, Vol. I, p. 318, unjustifiably to the present writer, extends this group to the central figure holding the cup in the Prado 'Los Borrachos' (No. 1170), to the kneeling king in the Prado 'Adoration' (No. 1166) and to the right-hand figure in the 'Music Players', Berlin (No. 413 F.). (12) The Budapest and other related pictures are discussed by C. Pemán, 'Acerca de los Llamados Almuerzos Velasqueños, in Arch. Esp. de Arte, Vol. XXXIV, 1961, p. 303 ff. For a comparison with Zurbarán's(?) S. John writing the Apocalypse, Barcelona (Coll. Prat) see D. Angulo Iñiguez in Arch. Esp. de Arte, Vol. XVII, 1944, p. 4. (13) See note 15; also C. B. Curtis, Velázquez and Murillo, 1883, No. 19; E. de Gué Trapier, Velázquez, 1948, p. 38; C. Justi, loc. cit. (14) A. F. Calvert and C. G. Hartley, Velázquez, p. 33, dated No. 6264, ca. 1617; J. Allende-Salazar, Velázquez, Klassiker der Kunst, 1925, p. 9, ca. 1618; A. L. Mayer, Velázquez, A Catalogue Raisonné, 1936, No. 35, about 1618; E. Lafuente, Velázquez, 1943, No. XIV, ca. 1619; Velázquez, with an introduction by José Ortega y Gasset, 1954, No. 19, ca. 1617; K. Gerstenberg, Diego Velázquez, 1957, pp. 71 and 75, ca. 1617; A. Gaya Nuño, Pintura Española fuera de España, 1958, No. 2821, ca. 1617–18. (15) J. A. Cean Bermudez, Diccionario Historico, etc., Vol. 5, 1800, p. 179: 'Sevilla. Cármen Calzado. Una Concepcion y un S. Juan Evangelista escribiendo el Apocalipsis, colocados en la sala de capítulo: pertenecen al primer tiempo de Velázquez'. (16) Letter from Bartholomew to George Frere, from Peru 23 December 1814 (copy in the N.G. archives): '. . . He [Hoppner] perhaps can tell you . . . the name of the Dean (or whatever he was) of the cathedral of Seville (but I know he was brother of the Archbishop) of whom I purchased them—He had bought them of the Convent upon condition of furnishing them with copies, and they were at the painters for this purpose when I bought them. . . .' (17) Letter from George Frere to Bartholomew Frere, 26 July 1813 (copy in the N.G. archives). This shows that the pictures had recently been moved from 'Hoppner's Lumber Garrett' to George Frere's house in Brunswick Square. [Sir] William [Maxwell] Stirling, Annals of the Artists in Spain, 1848, Vol. III, p. 1450, records them in the house of Barth. Frere, 45 Bedford Square. (18) Letter to The Times, 22 June 1956, from Philip Frere, an executor: 'Bartholomew Frere (who was married in 1817 by proxy to a Spanish lady who died in Spain in the autumn of that year, before ever meeting her husband) lived on in England until 1851, and nothing more was heard about the pictures until 1878, when a letter was received by Messrs. Frere & Co., of Lincoln's Inn Fields, from Messrs. Child & Co., the bankers, intimating that in consequence of the forthcoming demolition of Temple Bar they would have to give up the rooms over the archway, used for storage purposes, and would be glad to be relieved of some pictures and boxes labelled "B. Frere" which had been there in safe custody since the early 1830's [sic]'. Curtis (see note 13) records the two pictures in 1883 as the property of Bartle Frere. Philip Frere continues in The Times letter: 'These pictures [from Child's Bank], which included the two Velázquez mentioned in your announcement, eventually devolved upon the late Mr. Laurie Frere. . . .'

ESAIAS VAN DE VELDE
ca. 1590(?)–1630

Dutch School; worked at Haarlem and The Hague.

6269   A WINTER LANDSCAPE

Bought out of the Colnaghi Fund in 1957.
Oil on oak, $10\frac{3}{16} \times 11\frac{15}{16}$ (0·259 × 0·304).
Signed: E.v. VELDE. 1623.

Simon VOUET
1590–1649

French School. Baptised in Paris, 9 January 1590, the son of a minor painter. Vouet must have been apprenticed early; he is recorded as coming to England to paint at the age of fourteen. In 1611 he travelled to Constantinople and in the following year went to Venice. At the end of 1613 he went to Rome, where he seems to have remained, with occasional journeys to other Italian cities, until 1627. In that year he returned to Paris, summoned by Louis XIII. He was much employed by the French Crown in the Louvre Palace and elsewhere and worked also for Richelieu. Despite his success as the leading decorative painter in Paris, he was not a founder member of the Académie Royale established in 1648. Among his pupils were Le Sueur (q.v.), Mignard and Le Brun.

Vouet was much influenced by Italian art, as a young man especially by Caravaggio. Later under the influence of Veronese he gradually evolved a decorative, somewhat mannerist style. It has been well said of him that 'his influence on French painting was greater than his real quality as an artist might lead one to expect'.[1]

6292   CERES

Oil on canvas, $58\frac{1}{8} \times 74\frac{5}{8}$ (1·476 × 1·887). Apparently in excellent condition.

The picture is a recent discovery, as well as the work of a painter who has himself only recently been re-discovered, or, rather, studied in accordance with his merits. The contemporary and to some extent the rival of Poussin, Vouet was a very different kind of artist whose aims were in the first place decorative.

This is probably one of three canvases painted by him to decorate a small cabinet in the Hôtel de Bullion in Paris, in or ca. 1634.[2] The Hôtel was a luxurious building erected for Claude de Bullion (1570–1640), Surintendant des Finances, and Vouet at the same time decorated the gallery with an 'Odyssey' series, as well as working on a larger cabinet. The contract for all his decorations in the Hôtel was signed on 1 March 1634 and all the work was required to be finished by the end of that year.[3] There was no specification of what pictures should be painted for the small cabinet, but there are later references to a 'Hunt' with Diana and Actaeon, a 'Vintage' with Silenus and Satyrs, and a 'Harvest' 'with Ceres and cupids harvesting'.[4]

The last seems very likely to be No. 6292. It has recently been suggested that it is not the picture itself but a cartoon based on the composition and executed for the tapestries which were made of the series,[5] the reason advanced being the signs of hasty execution in the present painting. Since neither of the other two pictures from the small cabinet series has, it seems, survived, it is not possible to make comparisons of handling with them. While it is true that some other perhaps comparable pictures by Vouet appear more 'finished', it must also be noted that he had a considerable amount of work to do for the Hôtel de Bullion in ten months of 1634, if he was to keep to the contract. The pictures in the small cabinet would probably rank as the least important, or the last to be executed, and it would hardly be surprising if they betrayed signs of haste. Paradoxically enough therefore, the rapidity of execution certainly detectable in No. 6292 could well be evidence that it *is* from the Hôtel de Bullion series. Indeed, its spontaneity has a masterly touch suggesting not a repetition but a freshly created work of art, and its decorative air is almost rococo in style. Not only is the landscape one of the most remarkable painted by Vouet, but its handling and tone anticipate the achievements of the great French decorative painter of the following century, Boucher. It was bought from the Galerie Heim, Paris, in 1958 out of the Henry Oppenheimer Fund, with a contribution from Mr. Edgar Ivens.

EXHIBITED: 1958, Galerie Heim, Paris, *Tableaux de Maîtres Anciens*, No. 4.

NOTES: (1) A. Blunt, *Art and Architecture in France 1500–1700*, 1957 ed., p. 146. (2) A note on the picture by Y. Picart, with supplementary information from D. Mahon, was published in the *Burlington Magazine*, January 1959, pp. 27–28. (3) The contract was published by M. Charageat in an article on work commissioned by Bullion in *Bulletin de la Société de l'Histoire de l'Art Français*, 1927, p. 179 ff. Vouet also worked in Bullion's country house. (4) The earliest reference to exactly what pictures by Vouet are in the small cabinet is given by Dézallier d'Argenville in *Voyage Pittoresque de Paris* (4th edition), 1765, p. 174: the point made by Mahon, *loc. cit*. (5) See the comments of W. R. Crelly, *The Paintings of Simon Vouet*, 1962, p. 170 ff.

ROGIER VAN DER WEYDEN
ca. 1399–1464

Early Netherlandish School; from Tournai; worked in Brussels.

6265 'PIETÀ' WITH SS. JEROME AND DOMINIC(?) AND A DONOR

On the left, S. Jerome (whose lion is descending the hill behind) with the donor; on the right, S. Dominic(?).

Oil on oak, painted surface, $14 \times 17\frac{3}{4}$ (0·355 × 0·45). Cleaned on acquisition.[1]

Another picture of the '*Pietà*' by van der Weyden, in the Capilla Real at Granada,[2] is believed to be earlier than No. 6265, which may thus be said to have evolved from it. There, in a vertical frame, the figures are compressed within an elaborately sculptured setting of architecture; here the landscape is more closely united with the figures, even if, in order to intensify the tragedy, a large part of the delicious prospect is shut off by Golgotha.

This group of the '*Pietà*' was much admired, to judge by the number of variants in which his own hand is to be recognised in different degrees.[3] The National Gallery picture, attributed to van der Weyden by Friedländer and others,[4] is now generally recognised as the best. In serious characterisation and in brilliance of execution it would hold its own as a companion to any of his pictures on a small scale. The acquisition was of special importance for the National Gallery, where van der Weyden, perhaps the dominant influence in the 15th century in Flanders and throughout the greater part of northern Europe, had previously been inadequately represented. There is the 'Portrait of a Lady'; but 'The Magdalen reading', though a beautiful work, is a fragment and 'The Exhumation of S. Hubert' is apparently executed by a follower.[5]

No. 6265 was in the collection of the Earl of Powis by 1895.[6] It was acquired in 1956 from the Earl of Powis through Thomas Agnew and Sons in part payment of estate duty under the terms of the Finance Act, 1956. It was the first picture to be acquired by the nation in this way.

EXHIBITED: 1902, Burlington Fine Arts Club, No. 27;[7] 1906, Guildhall, No. 9; 1925, Agnew, No. 33; 1927, Royal Academy, No. 27 and 1953–54, No. 17; 1956, Bruges, No. 4.

NOTES: (1) In excellent condition, though blisters had to be laid. The crimson glaze of the Virgin's mantle was found to be somewhat worn, and little remained of her halo. Some earlier retouchings were left along a horizontal crack just below the centre. A few small corrections made by the artist, especially on Christ's body, have become visible with time. (2) Reproduced in the *Gazette des Beaux-Arts*, 1908, Vol. II, p. 301. It is part of a triptych, of which two panels are at Granada, the third in New York. A repetition, now usually assigned to Rogier's studio, of the triptych is in the Berlin Museum; this is reproduced in the Berlin Illustrations and elsewhere, *e.g.*, Panofsky (see below), Pls. 180 and 182. (3) Brussels, '*Pietà* with SS. John and Mary Magdalen', panel, 12¾ × 18⅜ (0·322 × 0·472), exhibited 1953–54, London, R.A., No. 15, reproduced in *Catalogue de la Peinture Ancienne*, Brussels, 1949, Pl. VI; Madrid, '*Pietà* with S. John and a Donor', panel, 18½ × 13¾ (0·47 × 0·35) with an arched top, reproduced in F. J. Sánchez Cantón, *The Prado Museum*, 1949, Pl. CXC; Berlin, identical with the Prado picture but rectangular, reproduced in the Berlin Illustrations. (4) Friedländer, *Die Altniederländische Malerei*, Vol. II, No. 20, as *ca.* 1450. Cf. further what Friedländer says in the *Repertorium für Kunstwissenschaft*, 1903, p. 70 and 1906, pp. 574–75. Hulin in the Memorial *Catalogue of the Loan Exhibition of Flemish and Belgian Art* at the Royal Academy, 1927, notes to Nos. 27 and 31, dates No. 6265 *ca.* 1440, and comments on its relationship to other variants; cf. also a long discussion of these relationships by Otto Seeck in the *Zeitschrift für bildende Kunst*, 1907, pp. 197 ff. There are some not very definite comments on the picture by Weale in *The Burlington Magazine*, Vol. I, 1903, p. 205 and Vol. IX, 1906, p. 186. Panofsky, *Early Netherlandish Painting*, 1953, Vol. I, p. 462 (note 4 to p. 261): 'According to the experts, the best of these variations . . . is the "*Pietà* with St. Jerome, St. Dominic and a Donor" in the Collection of the Earl of Powis . . . which is, however, not known to this writer'. (5) See Martin Davies, *National Gallery Catalogues, Early Netherlandish School*, 2nd edition, 1955, Nos. 1433, 654 and 783. (6) This date is on a label, formerly on the back of the picture. (7) For the identity, see *The Athenaeum*, 31 January 1903, p. 154.

RICHARD WILSON
1714–1782

British School; worked in London, and elsewhere in England; 1748–55 in Italy.

6196 HOLT BRIDGE, THE RIVER DEE

Oil on canvas, 58½ × 76½ (1·490 × 1·940).
See No. 6197.

6197 THE VALLEY OF THE DEE(?)

Oil on canvas, 58½ × 76½ (1·490 × 1·940).
Companion piece to No. 6196 above. Both were bought from the Colnaghi Fund, 1953.

Philips WOUWERMANS
1619–1668

Dutch School; worked in his native Haarlem.

6263 CAVALRY MAKING A SORTIE FROM A FORT ON A HILL

Oil on canvas, $54\frac{3}{4} \times 75$ ($1 \cdot 390 \times 1 \cdot 905$).
Signed and dated: *PHILWowermans/A* (o?) *1646* (PHIL in monogram).
Bought out of the Annual Grant in 1956.

Joachim WTEWAEL
ca. 1566–1638

Dutch School; worked in Utrecht.

6334 THE JUDGMENT OF PARIS

Oil on oak, $23\frac{1}{2} \times 31\frac{1}{8}$ ($0 \cdot 597 \times 0 \cdot 791$).
Signed and dated, bottom left: *Jo wte.wael/fecit/An° 1615* (Jo in monogram).
Bequeathed by Claude Dickason Rotch, 1962.

CHRONOLOGICAL LIST OF ARTISTS

Represented in the Exhibition of Acquisitions, 1953–62

UCCELLO (*ca.* 1397–1475): No. 6294
VAN DER WEYDEN (*ca.* 1399–1464): No. 6265
MEMLINC (Active 1465, d. 1494): No. 6275
LEONARDO DA VINCI (1452–1519): No. 6337
QUINTEN MASSYS (1465/6–1530): No. 6282
GIORGIONE (d. 1510): No. 6307
ALBRECHT ALTDORFER (*ca.* 1480–1538): No. 6320
EL GRECO (1541–1614): No. 6260
DOMENICHINO (1581–1641): Nos. 6284–91
STROZZI (1581–1644): No. 6321
LASTMAN (1583–1633): No. 6272
VOUET (1590–1649): No. 6292
LOUIS LE NAIN (*ca.* 1593–1648): No. 6331
JORDAENS (1593–1678): No. 6293
NICOLAS POUSSIN (1594?–1665): No. 6277
VELÁZQUEZ (1599–1660): No. 6264
DE CHAMPAIGNE (1602–1674): No. 6276
LA HIRE (1606–1656): No. 6329
REMBRANDT (1609–1669): Nos. 6274 and 6300
LE SUEUR (1616–1655): No. 6299
MURILLO (1617–1682): No. 6153
CAVALLINO (1616–54/6): No. 6297
GIORDANO (1634/5–1705): No. 6327
HOBBEMA (1638–1709): No. 6138
DE TROY (1679–1752): No. 6330
GIOVANNI BATTISTA PITTONI (1687–1767): No. 6279
GIOVANNI BATTISTA TIEPOLO (1696–1770): Nos. 6273 and 6302–05
BATONI (1708–1787): Nos. 6308 and 6316
GAINSBOROUGH (1727–1788): Nos. 6209 and 6301
DELACROIX (1798–1863): No. 6262
DEGAS (1834–1917): No. 6295
CÉZANNE (1839–1906): No. 6195
MONET (1840–1926): No. 6278
RENOIR (1841–1919): Nos. 6306, 6317–18 and 6319

NUMERICAL INDEX OF PICTURES

In order of acquisition

6280   CORNELIUS JOHNSON: Portrait of a Lady

6281   GAINSBOROUGH, Style of: Landscape

6282   MASSYS: The Virgin and Child enthroned, with four Angels

6284   Apollo slaying the Nymph Coronis

6285   The Punishment of Midas

6286   The Transformation of Cyparissus

6287   DOMENICHINO: Apollo and Daphne

6288   The Flaying of Marsyas

6289   Neptune and Apollo advising Laomedon on the Building of Troy

6290   Apollo killing the Cyclops

6291   Mercury stealing the Herds of Admetus guarded by Apollo

6292   VOUET: Ceres

6293   JORDAENS: Portrait of a Man and his Wife

6294   UCCELLO: S. George and the Dragon

6295   DEGAS: *Après le bain, femme s'essuyant* (pastel)

6296   DU JARDIN: The Conversion of S. Paul

6297   CAVALLINO: The Finding of Moses

6298   ROSA: Landscape, with Tobias and the Angel

6299   LE SUEUR: S. Paul preaching at Ephesus

6300   REMBRANDT: Equestrian Portrait

6301   GAINSBOROUGH: Mr. and Mrs. Andrews

6302   Two Orientals standing

6303   G. B. TIEPOLO: Rinaldo looking in the Magic Mirror

6304   A seated Man and a Girl with a Pitcher

6305   Two Orientals seated under a Tree

6306   RENOIR: Portrait of Madame Edwards

6307   GIORGIONE: Sunset Landscape with S. Roch(?), S. George and S. Anthony ('*Il Tramonto*')

6308   P. G. BATONI: Mr. Scott of Banksfee

6309   *La Plage à Trouville*

6310   *La Plage à Trouville*

6311   BOUDIN: *Village au bord d'une Rivière*

6312   *La Plage de Trouville*

6313   *Laveuses au bord de l'Eau*

6316   P. G. BATONI: Time destroying Beauty

6317   *La Danseuse au tambourin*

6318   RENOIR: *La Danseuse aux castagnettes*

6319   *Baigneuse se coiffant*

6320   ALTDORFER: Landscape with a Footbridge

6321   STROZZI: An Allegory of Fame

6322   GOYA: The Duke of Wellington

6323   DAUBIGNY: View on the Oise with Boat and Laundress

6324   Landscape with Cattle by a Stream

6325   HARPIGNIES: *Une Soirée d'Automne*

6327   GIORDANO: The Martyrdom of S. Januarius

6320   ALTDORFER : Landscape with a Footbridge

6308 P. G. BATONI: Mr. Scott of Banksfee

6316 P. G. BATONI: Time destroying Beauty

6309   BOUDIN: *La Plage à Trouville*

6310   BOUDIN: *La Plage à Trouville*

6311   BOUDIN : *Village au bord d'une Rivière*

6312   BOUDIN : *La Plage de Trouville*

6313 BOUDIN : *Laveuses au bord de l'Eau*

6297   Cavallino : The Finding of Moses

6195   CÉZANNE: *La Vieille au chapelet*

6276   P. DE CHAMPAIGNE: The Vision of S. Joseph

6336   CLAESZ., Ascribed: Still Life

6160   COQUES, Ascribed: Portrait of a Young Lady in Black

6339   COROT: *Dardagny—Un Chemin dans la Campagne, le Matin*

6340   COROT: *La Charrette. Souvenir de Saintry*

6323 DAUBIGNY: View on the Oise with Boat and Laundress

6324 DAUBIGNY : Landscape with Cattle by a Stream

6295 DEGAS: *Après le Bain, Femme s'essuyant* (pastel)

6262   DELACROIX: Ovid among the Scythians

6330 DE TROY: Jason swearing eternal affection to Medea

6284   DOMENICHINO: Apollo slaying the Nymph Coronis

6285 DOMENICHINO: The Punishment of Midas

6286 DOMENICHINO: The Transformation of Cyparissus

6287   DOMENICHINO: Apollo and Daphne

6288   DOMENICHINO : The Flaying of Marsyas

6289   DOMENICHINO: Neptune and Apollo advising Laomedon on the building of Troy

6290 DOMENICHINO: Apollo killing the Cyclops

6291 DOMENICHINO: Mercury stealing the herds of Admetus guarded by Apollo

6266 FLORENTINE SCHOOL, 15th century: The Virgin and Child

6335 JAN FYT: Still Life with Fruit and Game

6301 GAINSBOROUGH: Mr. and Mrs. Andrews

6209 GAINSBOROUGH: The Morning Walk

6242   GAINSBOROUGH: Gainsborough Dupont

6281　Style of GAINSBOROUGH : Landscape

6229 GIAQUINTO: The Crowning of Spain (?)

6327   GIORDANO: The Martyrdom of S. Januarius

6307   GIORGIONE: Sunset Landscape with S. Roch (?), S. George and S. Anthony (*Il Tramonto*)

6322   GOYA: The Duke of Wellington

6154   VAN GOYEN: A River Scene, with a Hut on an Island

6155   Van Goyen: A River Scene, with Fishermen hauling a Net

6156 GUARDI: Venice: The Punta della Dogana

6157 GUARDI: Venice: The Giudecca with the Zitelle

6260   EL GRECO: The Adoration of the Name of Jesus

6325　Harpignies: *Une Soirée d'Automne*

6138   HOBBEMA: The Herring Packers' Tower, Amsterdam

6296   DU JARDIN: The Conversion of S. Paul

6333   HOPPNER: Portrait of Sir George Beaumont

6280   CORNELIUS JOHNSON: Portrait of a Lady

6293   JORDAENS: Portrait of a Man and His Wife

6329   LA HIRE: Allegorical Figure of Grammar

6272 PIETER LASTMAN: Juno discovering Jupiter with Io

6331   LE NAIN : The Adoration of the Shepherds

6337   LEONARDO DA VINCI: The Virgin and Child with S. Anne
and S. John the Baptist (cartoon)

6299   LE SUEUR: S. Paul preaching at Ephesus

6275   MEMLINC: The Virgin and Child with Saints, Angels and Donors
(The Donne Triptych) (centre panel)

6275   MEMLINC: The Virgin and Child with Saints, Angels and Donors
(The Donne Triptych) (left and right panels)

6282 MASSYS: The Virgin and Child enthroned, with four Angels

6253 J.-F. Millet, Ascribed: Landscape with Buildings

6278   MONET : *L'Inondation*

Bart.^{us} Murillo seipsum depin
gens pro filiorum votis ac preci
bus explendis

6153   MURILLO : Self-Portrait

6254　Neapolitan School, 18th century: Portrait of a Lady

6161 NETHERLANDISH SCHOOL, 16th century: A Little Girl
with a Basket of Cherries

6328   PELLEGRINI: Sketch for 'The Marriage of the Elector Palatine and Anna Maria Luisa de' Medici'

6332   PELLEGRINI: Rebecca at the Well

6279   G. B. PITTONI: The Nativity, with God the Father and the
Holy Ghost

6277   NICOLAS POUSSIN: The Adoration of the Shepherds

6274   REMBRANDT: An Old Man in an Armchair (*before cleaning*)

6300   REMBRANDT: Equestrian Portrait

6270   GUIDO RENI: The Adoration of the Shepherds

6306　RENOIR : Portrait of Madame Edwards

6317   RENOIR: *La Danseuse au tambourin*

6318   RENOIR: *La Danseuse aux castagnettes*

6319   RENOIR: *Baigneuse se coiffant*

6298 ROSA : Landscape, with Tobias and the Angel

6338 S. VAN RUYSDAEL: A View of Deventer

6321 STROZZI: An Allegory of Fame

6273   G. B. TIEPOLO: The Trinity appearing to S. Clement (?)

6302　G. B. Tiepolo: Two Orientals standing

6303　G. B. Tiepolo: Rinaldo looking in the Magic Mirror

6304   G. B. TIEPOLO: A seated Man and a Girl with a Pitcher

6305   G. B. TIEPOLO: Two Orientals under a Pine-Tree

6294   Uccello: S. George and the Dragon

6264   VELÁZQUEZ: S. John on the Island of Patmos

6269   E. van de Velde : A Winter Landscape

6292 VOUET: Ceres

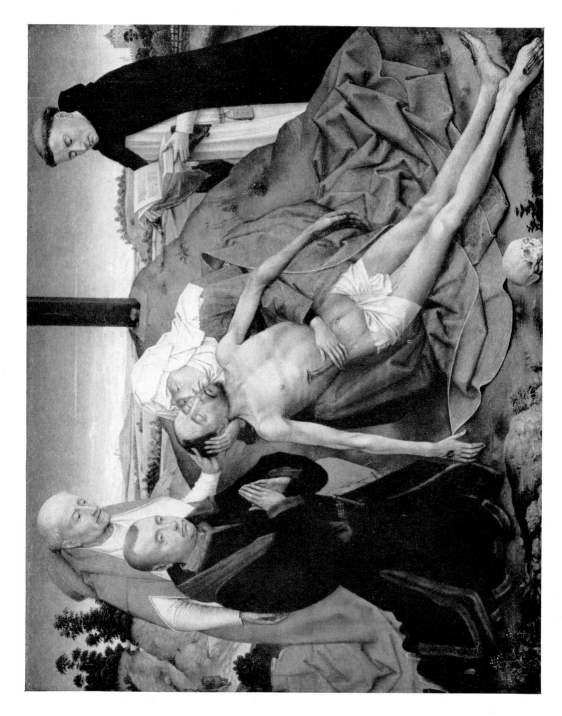

6265 VAN DER WEYDEN: *Pietà*, with SS. Jerome and Dominic (?) and a Donor

6196   WILSON: Holt Bridge, the River Dee

6197   WILSON: The Valley of the Dee

6263 Wouwermans : Cavalry making a Sortie from a Fort on a Hill

6334   WTEWAEL : The Judgment of Paris